Augmenting the Canon

Recent Acquisitions of American Neo-Classical Decorative Arts

Augmenting the Canon

Recent Acquisitions of American Neo-Classical Decorative Arts

Elizabeth Feld

Stuart P. Feld

December 13, 2018 – February 6, 2019

Hirschl & Adler Galleries

The Fuller Building

41 East 57th Street

New York, New York 10022

212.535.8810

www.HirschlAndAdler.com

CONTENTS

INTRODUCTION

When The American Wing at The Metropolitan Museum of Art, New York, opened in a purpose-built addition in 1924, it featured about twenty period rooms dating stylistically from around 1640 to the first quarter of the nineteenth century, together with a group of "period" spaces that were meant to evoke the aesthetics of the Pilgrim century, the eighteenth century, and the early Federal era. These were outfitted with a variety of furniture and other decorative arts covering the same chronology, much courtesy of the acquisition of collections formed by H. Eugene Bolles (purchased through funding by Mrs. Russell Sage), George S. Palmer, Louis Guerineau Myers, George Coe Graves, and Mrs. J. Insley Blair. With very few exceptions, there was little in the furniture collection that post-dated the early reeded furniture of Duncan Phyfe that had been the subject of a monographic exhibition at The Metropolitan Museum in 1922, and a book by Met curator Charles Over Cornelius published in the same year. In his introduction, Cornelius wrote that the goal of the exhibition had been "to present at least all the general known types of furniture from Phyfe's *best period* [our emphasis]," thus acknowledging that the delicate scale of Phyfe's early designs was acceptable, while Phyfe's gutsier and bolder later work of equal quality was beyond the aesthetics of that moment.

As late as the 1960s, there was not a single Tiffany Studios lamp in The Met's collection, although through the benefaction of H. O. Havemeyer in 1896 and through a loan from the Tiffany Foundation in 1925 (which became a gift in 1951), The Metropolitan Museum already had a formidable collection of Tiffany glass, which became the subject of one of the first articles on Tiffany glass in modern times when it was published in the Museum's *Bulletin* in November 1962.

Numerous acquisitions were made in the four decades following the opening of The American Wing, but most were in keeping with the parameters that had governed the Museum's early collections of Americana.

Attributed to Isaac Vose & Son,
with Thomas Seymour as foreman
Boston
Work Table, about 1819–24
CAT. 12

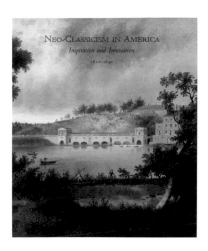

Neo-Classicism in America
Exhibition catalogue, 1991

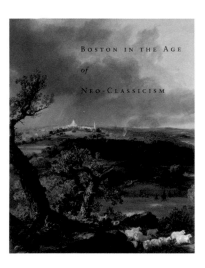

Boston in the Age of Neo-Classicism
Exhibition catalogue, 1999

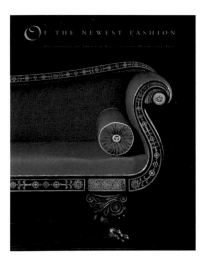

Of the Newest Fashion
Exhibition catalogue, 2001

In 1963 Berry B. Tracy organized the decorative arts section of the exhibition, *Classical America, 1815–1845*, at the Newark Museum, which made an important impact on those interested in somewhat later American decorative arts. In the following year, Tracy was hired as a curator in The American Wing at The Met. And then, in 1965, The Metropolitan put on view more than 400 American paintings from its permanent collection, bringing to light, for the first time, in an exhibition called *Three Centuries of American Painting*, the extraordinary quality and encyclopedic range of a collection that less than two decades earlier had hardly been a footnote in a paintings department that largely emphasized its holdings in European art. The impetus fostered by this exhibition, followed in 1966 by *Two Hundred Years of Watercolor Painting in America*, also stimulated interest in the other arts of the nineteenth century and beyond.

Not long thereafter, in contemplating a series of celebratory exhibitions to mark the hundredth anniversary of the founding of The Metropolitan Museum in 1870, the idea of *19th-Century America* was hatched to celebrate the century that gave birth to the Museum. But the Museum continued to have few objects in its collection to support such an endeavor, except for some very early acquisitions of later nineteenth-century material to demonstrate, as outlined in the Museum's original charter, "the application of arts to manufacture and practical life." And with few funds to dedicate to more experimental acquisitions, architectural historian and critic Edgar Kaufman, Jr., was solicited to underwrite some initial purchases.

19th-Century America premiered in April 1970, and for the first time presented, in a series of period rooms and galleries, the entire panorama of the arts of the United States from the early 1800s to slightly beyond 1900. Rightly, this extraordinary gathering of material was immediately heralded as a model for an expanded American Wing, which was itself inaugurated ten years later. And, soon enough, museums across the country, and private collectors as well, to say nothing of a new generation of dealers, caught on to these new collectibles, and a whole new industry was begun.

In 1983, Hirschl & Adler entered the nineteenth-century decorative arts market, and several years later showed a vignette of Victorian Renaissance furniture and a small case of early ninetheenth-century "Old Paris" porcelain at the 1986 edition of the Winter Antiques Show. Within twenty minutes after the opening of the gala preview, all had been sold. Success breeds success, and we gradually began to accumulate the best of the decorative arts from the Neo-Classical period to the Arts and Crafts movement. Our January presentations became more and more comprehensive, and museums and private collectors beat a path to our door in search of the best material of the nineteenth century.

Installation view, *The World of Duncan Phyfe:*
The Arts of New York, 1800–1847, 2011
Hirschl & Adler Galleries, New York

For Work & for Play
Exhibition catalogue, 2007

In 1991, we organized our first formal exhibition of decorative arts, *Neo-Classicism in America: Inspiration and Innovation, 1810–1840*, in which we featured groupings of material from Boston, New York, Philadelphia, and Baltimore, both from the gallery's collection as well as loans from Winterthur, The Metropolitan Museum, the Brooklyn Museum, the firms of Israel Sack, Alexander Acevedo, Anthony Stuempfig, and Richard York, and from the private collections of Richard and Gloria Manney and others. Just two years later, in 1993, Wendy Cooper opened *Classical Taste in America, 1810–1840* at the Baltimore Museum of Art, which significantly expanded upon the scope and depth of *Classical America* from three decades earlier.

And what followed was a remarkable series of exhibitions and accompanying catalogues. There was *Honoré Lannuier: Cabinetmaker from Paris* at The Met in 1998. The same year brought *Boston in the Age of Neo-Classicism, 1810–1840*, at Hirschl & Adler, followed by three more general surveys, *Of the Newest Fashion: Masterpieces of American Neo-Classical Decorative Arts* in 2001, *For Work & For*

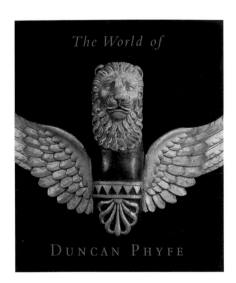

The World of Duncan Phyfe
Exhibition catalogue, 2011

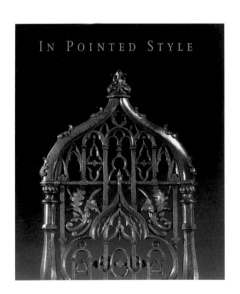

In Pointed Style
Exhibition catalogue, 2006

Play in 2007, and *Very Rich and Handsome* in 2014. In 2011, The Metropolitan Museum organized a monographic survey of the long and varied career of Duncan Phyfe, which was put into a broader New York context in Hirschl & Adler's concurrent *The World of Duncan Phyfe: The Arts of New York, 1800–1847*. In contrast to the focused Phyfe exhibition at The Met in 1922, these exhibitions dramatically expanded the canon and unlocked our understanding of the full range of the work of Phyfe and his contemporaries.

Boston also received its due with Robert Mussey's catalogue, *The Masterworks of Thomas Seymour*, which documented an impressive exhibition at the Peabody Essex Museum in Salem, Massachusetts, in 2003. And his 2018 collaboration with Clark Pearce at the Massachusetts Historical Society, Boston, on the various incarnations of cabinetmaker Isaac Vose and his association with his son, and with Joshua Coates, Thomas Seymour, and Thomas Wightman, not only significantly enhanced our understanding of Vose's work, but also expanded our knowledge of Seymour's later work while he was the foreman in the Vose shop, and of the unique contribution of carver extraordinaire, Thomas Wightman. Alas, no one has yet fully tackled the Philadelphia scene, either globally, or individually with respect to the likes of Joseph Barry, or a more updated view of Anthony Gabriel Quervelle beyond Robert Smith's series of articles in *The Magazine Antiques* published between 1964 and 1974.

And, along the way, other specialized areas have received attention, among them the Museum of Fine Arts, Houston's *The Gothic Revival Style in America* of 1976, followed thirty years later by Hirschl & Adler's *In Pointed Style: The Gothic Revival in America, 1800–1860*. In 1987, the Museum of Fine Arts, Houston organized *Marks of Achievement: Four Centuries of American Presentation Silver*, which chronicled the history of presentation silver in the United States. And in 2007, Winterthur orchestrated an encyclopedic exhibition of the silver of Thomas Fletcher and Sidney Gardiner, again accompanied by a catalogue that will remain a definitive text on the subject for generations to come.

Dozens and dozens of other general and specialized exhibitions have taken place, and scores of publications, again both general and tightly focused, have been issued, which, cumulatively, have significantly enhanced our understanding of a century that not so very long ago was almost completely ignored and certainly not understood.

Classical America at the Newark Museum in 1963 was a watershed exhibition, but with the dramatically expanded archive of furniture, silver, lighting, ceramics, and glass, and the accompanying information that has by now been assembled, our knowledge—the canon—is today of a different magnitude. And

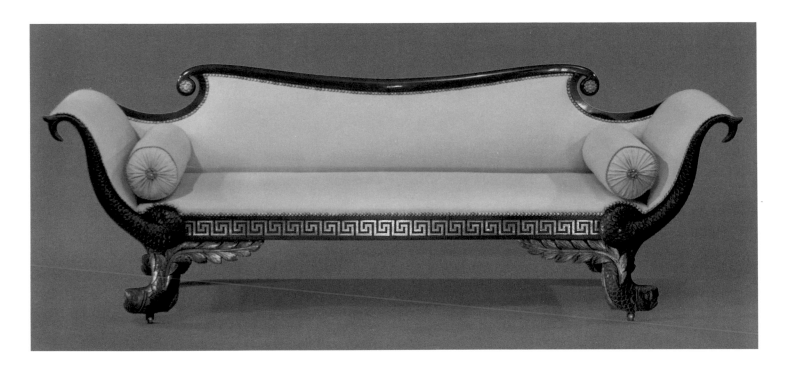

an exhibition such as *Augmenting the Canon* presents, as it does, a number of objects that have not previously been illustrated and discussed, and will serve to continue to expand our knowledge of this fascinating moment that paralleled important historical developments in the United States.

And the work continues. At Hirschl & Adler, for example, we have developed an extensive archive devoted to nineteenth-century American furniture, lighting, silver, ceramics, and glass. We have organized individual "catalogues' raisonnés" of important forms, including, for example, a photographic and documentary archive of thirteen dolphin sofas of the form of the one shown at Newark in 1963 (fig. 1)—and which was acquired by The Metropolitan Museum in 1965—although we still do not know either who made them, or even exactly where they were made. And with respect to the Phyfe *Secrétaire à Abattant*, which is catalogue no. 4 in this exhibition, we have organized an archive that documents the stylistic and chronological development of the form through a dozen examples stretching from the late 1810s to the early 1840s. But we are still far from a complete understanding of the field. Although in the area of Philadelphia Chippendale furniture, for example, we know the names of the carvers Bernard Jugiez (active 1767–died 1815), Nicholas Bernard (1732–1788), Hercules Courtenay (1736–1784), and James Reynolds (about 1739–1794), and many attributions have been made to them, in the Neo-Classical field, roughly a half-century younger, we know barely more than the name of Thomas Wightman, who worked as a carver for Thomas Seymour and other cabinetmakers in Boston

Installation view, *Very Rich & Handsome: American Neo-Classical Decorative Arts*, 2014
Hirschl & Adler Galleries, New York

in the first quarter of the nineteenth century. And whereas we recognize that the figural carvings on Charles-Honoré Lannuier's furniture are not all by the same hand, we have no idea who those very talented individuals were. But as the number of objects in this fascinating period increases, so will our knowledge of the individual craftsmen who created them lead to a more complete understanding of a significant moment in the history of the decorative arts in the United States.

Most antique furniture, even pieces that have survived in fine condition, have needed some degree of conservation — in the case of Neo-Classical furniture, after two-hundred years of, oftentimes, active use or benign neglect.

When furniture went out of fashion, it was often carted off to weekend and summer homes, and, indeed, some of our early "finds" were in antique shops and private homes in such places as Southampton, New York; Manchester, Massachusetts; and Southwest Harbor, Maine, and many watering spots and mountain retreats in between. They were thus preserved rather than discarded, but many suffered the consequences of unheated houses in which there were dramatic fluctuations in temperature and humidity. Frequently, the original French-polished surfaces were severely compromised, with their early appearance revealed only when original drawer knobs or pulls, or ormolu or gilt-brass mounts were removed. Early refinishers often simply brushed on coats of shellac or varnish or lacquer in an attempt to replicate the original finish, either not understanding the method by which that finish was accomplished, or attempting to circumvent the labor-intensive and thus expensive process of French polishing.

Similarly, there was little understanding with respect to gilded surfaces, and the important distinction between the aesthetics of oil and water gilding. Some works were cavalierly regessoed and regilded without any regard for what the original surface may have looked like. And painted *verde-antique* surfaces, which were intended to replicate the appearance of excavated bronze, were often "restored" with heavy coats of opaque black, green, or brown paint, the subtle glazes that were originally used by the likes of Duncan Phyfe and Charles-Honoré Lannuier thus hidden from view. On occasion, original paint has happily been exposed when later repainting has been carefully removed through conservation.

The restoration of the metalwork that was often an important part of the aesthetic of Neo-Classical furniture has also been misunderstood, including the important distinction between ormolu, and gilt brass or gilt bronze. Ormolu is gold plating on bronze, while gilt brass or gilt bronze is achieved through the application of a tinted lacquer. The ormolu mounts used on American Neo-Classical furniture were largely—but not exclusively—of French origin, while the lacquered hardware was most often an English import. Unless ormolu mounts have been abused, a light cleaning with ammonia will usually restore their original brilliance and the subtle variation of burnished and matte surfaces. In contrast, the gilt surfaces on metalwork, achieved with organic materials, have variously darkened or otherwise deteriorated, frequently beyond recognition. Before the manner in which their sparkly surfaces had originally been achieved was fully understood, many pieces of hardware were erroneously gold plated, producing an effect that was not in keeping with their original appearance.

The same can be said of the large variety of Birmingham, England-produced chandeliers, and Argand, sinumbra, and student lamps, as well as rare examples made in the United States, some of both of which were harshly cleaned and polished to feature a lacquered surface of raw brass or bronze instead of a replication of the original gilt and/or dark-brown patina.

A decade or so ago, Hirschl & Adler Galleries acquired a typical Duncan Phyfe trestle-base card table that had never been subjected to any kind of conservation or restoration (figs. 2A, 2B, 2C). The rosewood veneers, the areas that were paint-grained rosewood, and the striped maple border had all darkened to a point where there was little differentiation among them in terms of color or pattern. The brass inlay had tarnished, and the carved and gilded water leaves on the saber legs and the ormolu mount at the center of the skirt had lost their intended luster and now blended with their background to make them virtually invisible. In order to demonstrate the vast difference between what the artist had intended and how the piece had aged, we charged our cabinet shop with the task of cleaning the right half of the wooden surfaces, at which time the brass line inlay was exposed and polished, and then French polishing that part of the table to replicate its original finish. Similarly, the gilded carving was cleaned, two of the four brass toe caps and castors were stripped of the remaining deteriorated coats of lacquer and were refreshed with a tinted lacquer, and half the ormolu mount was cleaned, all to replicate their original appearance. And, lo and behold, a masterpiece of New York cabinetmaking was reborn—at least partially! After showing the piece in our exhibition, *Of the Newest Fashion: Masterpieces of American Neo-Classical Decorative Arts* in 2001, and at The Winter Antiques Show in 2003, where it was an eye-opener to many who understood for the first time the transformation that had taken place between the colorful, multi-textured work that had come out of the Duncan Phfye shop, and the dull, monochromatic piece that had come down to us after it had aged through nearly two hundred years, we had the conservation completed and it

Attributed to
Duncan Phyfe (1770–1854)
New York
Trestle-base Gaming Table, about 1820
Rosewood, amboyna, and mahogany,
variously paint-grained rosewood and gilded
(secondary woods: mahogany, maple, pine, and poplar),
with brass line inlay, ormolu mounts, gilt-brass toe
caps and castors, baize playing surface, and marble
paper lining the well, 29¾ in. high, 36 in. wide,
18⅛ in. deep; open: 36 in. x 36 in.

Private collection

FIG. 2A

Before conservation

FIG. 2B

After conservation of right half

FIG. 2C

After completed conservation

FIG. 2A

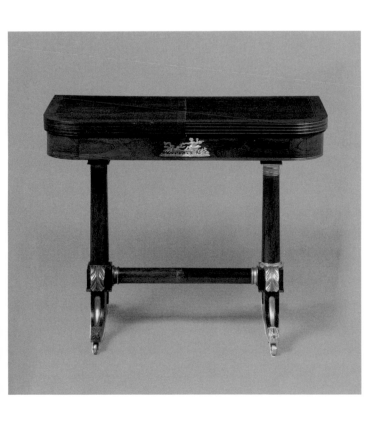

FIG. 2B

FIG. 2C

15

has since resided in a private collection. And just as our knowledge of the entire field of American Neo-Classical decorative arts has dramatically expanded since the days when The Metropolitan Museum would show only what it then perceived was Duncan Phyfe's "best period," so we have learned the intricacies of the conservation of this very beautiful—and very complex—furniture and other decorative arts from the early years of the nineteenth century. The lesson learned is that responsible restoration and stewardship honors both the intentions of the artist and the aesthetics of the period during which the pieces were made, and no more!

———————

In producing this catalogue and its accompanying exhibition, we are indebted to all who have preceded us who have cumulatively contributed to an understanding of an important era in the history of American decorative arts. One can only hope that Robert Mussey and Clark Pearce's recent exhibition and catalogue, *Rather Elegant Than Showy: The Classical Furniture of Isaac Vose*, will now stand as a beacon of the level of scholarship and understanding that will cast its light on all aspects of American art from the transformational years of the early Republic.

An exhibition of this kind relies on the goodwill and diligence of many people. First, we acknowledge the help of those who brought some of these beautiful objects to our attention. We also thank our extremely talented researchers, Carol Lowrey and Arlene Katz Nichols, who were able to unearth—or confirm— some of the more abstruse facts contained herein, mostly from long out-of-print sources. Our assistant, Yarden Elias, has seen the manuscript through many stages, and our longtime and cherished colleague Eric W. Baumgartner has helped to comb through and polish our prose. Eric must also be credited with most of the photographs reproduced in this publication, and for this we are profoundly grateful. A team of expert conservators has worked with meticulous care to bring various pieces back to their full glory. And our devoted registrars, Bill Blatz and Carlos Gonzalez, will, as always, complete an artistic installation for all to enjoy in our new gallery space. Once again, our talented designer Elizabeth Finger and The Studley Press have enabled us to share these thoughts and important works of art with you through this richly illustrated volume.

Although this catalogue documents only the decorative arts included in this exhibition, there will also be on view a complement of American paintings, watercolors, drawings, and sculpture from the Neo-Classical period.

ELIZABETH FELD AND STUART P. FELD

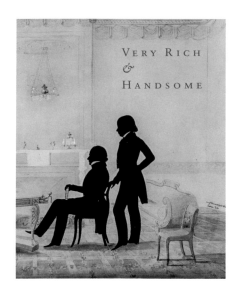

Very Rich & Handsome
Exhibition catalogue, 2014

Installation view, *Very Rich & Handsome: American Neo-Classical Decorative Arts*, 2014
Hirschl & Adler Galleries, New York

FURNITURE

1

Attributed to

JOSEPH BARRY

1757–1838

Philadelphia (active 1794–1833)

Récamier, about 1825

Mahogany (secondary woods: pine and poplar), with gilt-brass castors and bolster buttons, and upholstery, 34½ in. high, 90 in. long, 24⅜ in. deep

Inscribed (on a piece of paper, formerly attached to the front seat rail of the sofa, and now attached to the underside of the sofa): This sofa came from the William Brown family / at Market & Chestnut Sts was in the / parlor. When the house was dismantled / Elizabeth Norris Brown [illeg.] gave it to Fanny / Brown Coleman. When the house at Lebanon was dismantled Elizabeth Norris Brown took it.

FIG. 3

Thomas Sully (1783–1872)
Portrait of William Brown, 1833
Oil on canvas, 30 x 25 in.

Location unknown

In the bibliography of Philadelphia furniture of the Neo-Classical period, the name Anthony Gabriel Quervelle (1789–1856) has long dominated the field. Between September 1964 and January 1974, Robert Smith authored a series of five articles on Quervelle for *The Magazine Antiques*, and the number of pieces labeled by him has prompted a host of additional attributions. But despite a few important commissions, such as one he received from The White House in 1829, Quervelle's work rarely reached an ultimate level of design and craft that could place him in the exalted company of Duncan Phyfe and Charles-Honoré Lannuier in New York, and Thomas Seymour and Isaac Vose in Boston.

But that pantheon could include Joseph Barry, a London-trained cabinetmaker who first appeared in the Philadelphia Directory in 1794 and remained active there until 1833. Barry was the subject of several articles in *Antiques*, in January 1975 and May 1989, but he has never been subjected to the same myopic scrutiny as have Phyfe, Lannuier, and, most recently, Seymour and Vose. And with the scarcity of labeled and documented pieces, attributions remain the standard way to assign work to his shop. But the extraordinary labeled console table in the collection of The Metropolitan Museum of Art (Philadelphia Museum, 1976, p. 220 no. 180 illus.) establishes his exemplary level of work, and can justify the attribution to him of other works of comparable quality.

Among these is this extraordinary récamier made for William Brown (fig. 3) and his wife, Deborah Norris Brown, for their Philadelphia townhouse at 295 Chestnut Street, at the corner of Market Street. (As unlikely as that address would appear today, since Market and Chestnut Streets run parallel to one another, period maps show that Market Street turned south when it hit the Delaware River and intersected with Chestnut Street.) Although initially ascribed to Quervelle because of the large, carved shell fronting its arm, a motif that appears both in Quervelle's sketchbook in the collection of the Philadelphia Museum of Art and on numerous pieces by or attributed to him, the piece clearly surpasses the majority of his labeled and documented work.

Indeed, this récamier stands apart, both in its superb, well-integrated design and in the outstanding quality of its carving, which displays a delicacy and assuredness that is absent in the work of Quervelle and others working in Philadelphia at the time, but, nevertheless, partakes of the local style of flat and crisp carving.

2

Attributed to

JOSEPH BARRY

1757–1838

Philadelphia (active 1794–1833)

Monumental Pier Table with Brass Inlay, about 1815

Mahogany and rosewood (secondary woods: pine and poplar), with gilt-brass mounts, die-stamped brass inlay, some inset with ebony, mirror plate, and marble, 39⅛ in. high, 44¼ in. wide, 21⅞ in. deep

FIG. 4

Philadelphia

Pier Table, about 1815

Mahogany, with ormolu mounts, mirror plate, and specimen marble top, 39 in. high, 52½ in. wide, 30 in. deep

Private collection

When this large pier table was advertised by the firm of Ginsburg & Levy in *The Magazine Antiques* in November 1965 (p. 576), it was described as "certainly the work of Joseph B. Barry," and, with the focus given to American Neo-Classical furniture in the last half century, ever since Berry Tracy's landmark exhibition, *Classical America, 1815–1845*, at the Newark Museum in 1963, nothing has emerged that would challenge that attribution.

Qualitatively, the table, like the récamier ascribed to Barry (cat. 1), stands at the summit of American production in the early years of the nineteenth century, and bears various "hallmarks" of a Philadelphia style from about 1815. The pair of double columns at each end of the façade duplicates the format of another monumental table of Philadelphia origin (fig. 4; and Tracy et al., *19th-Century America*, no. 35 illus.), and, like it, may have been derived from the elevation of a wall-bed (*lit à couronne*) illustrated in Pierre de la Mésangère's *Collection de Meubles et Objets de Goût* (plate 519), which was published serially in Paris between 1802 and 1831 (as reproduced in Mussey and Pearce, *Rather Elegant*, p. 170 fig. 194). And the telescopic turnings that form the lowest register of the four columns are a feature that appears repeatedly in Philadelphia furniture of the period.

Most especially, however, the wide die-stamped brass inlay along the front and sides of the skirt is seen in a variety of patterns on a group of high-style Philadelphia furniture of the Neo-Classical period, and is surely the kind of ornament that Barry was referring to in an advertisement he placed in the Philadelphia *General Advertiser* for September 1, 1824, "2 Rich Sideboards, Buhl [*sic*] work," which has been the catalyst to assign to him various pieces that are so adorned. This would include a *secrétaire à abattant* in the collection of Hirschl & Adler Galleries (fig. 5); a suite of furniture from the Gratz family of Philadelphia in the collection of the Philadelphia Museum of Art (Philadelphia Museum, 1976, pp. 265–66 no. 221 illus.); and a bookcase on stand in the Linda and George Kaufman Collection at the National Gallery of Art, Washington, D.C. (Flanigan, pp. 220–21 no. 90 illus.). This type of ornamentation, which is also seen in the United States on a small group of furniture made by Vose & Coates and Co. of Boston, and Duncan Phyfe and Charles-Honoré Lannuier in New York, was ultimately derived from a style popularized by the French cabinetmaker, André Charles Boulle (1642–1732). The brass inlays were cer-

tainly acquired from the metalworking center of Birmingham, England, possibly, as Clark Pearce suggests in conjunction with his study of Isaac Vose, from the firm of James Barron, whose trade catalogue of 1814 includes "Highly polished Brass Ornaments for inlaying into hard wood" (*Rather Elegant*, p. 229). Barron was, likely not coincidentally, the source for a variety of drawer pulls signed "BARRONS / PATENT," as well as castors marked "BB&C°/PATENT" that appear on Vose furniture.

The circular brass collars that serve as "capitals" and "bases" to the columns were certainly not made with that purpose in mind, but, as is often the case with the use of imported gilt-brass and ormolu mounts on American furniture of this period, there is at times something of a "make-do" attitude based upon the limited variety of imported mounts available at a given moment. Cabinetmakers were thus motivated to adapt certain ornaments for purposes for which they were not initially intended. In this case, the gilt-brass collars are identical in form to those that were made to be used as decorative bands, or "capitals," at the tops of the legs of pianos (for examples, see Kuronen, pp. 323 fig. 10; 325 fig. 13; and 327 fig. 15), but here used quite differently, especially as they are stacked at the bottoms of the columns.

The present pier table is of unusually large scale, and thus takes its place beside two other oversized Philadelphia pier tables that must also be dated to about 1815: the great table labeled by Barry at The Metropolitan Museum that was made for Louis Clapier (1765–1838; see Philadelphia Museum, p. 220 no. 180 illus.), which, like the present table, refers to English Regency designs for inspiration; and the other table with double columns on its façade (fig. 4), which was likely influenced by a French Empire prototype.

FIG. 5

Attributed to Joseph B. Barry
Philadelphia
Secrétaire à Abattant, about 1820
Rosewood, partially ebonized, and satinwood
(secondary woods: cedar, mahogany, pine, and poplar),
with die-stamped brass inlay inset with ebony, brass locks
and hinges, and leather writing surface, blind-stamped
and tooled in gold, 65½ in. high, 42¾ in. wide,
21¾ in. deep; 42½ in. deep (with fall front open)

Collection of Hirschl & Adler Galleries, New York

3

PHILADELPHIA

Card Table with Lyre Base, about 1815

Mahogany, striped and bird's eye maple, and ebony
(secondary woods: cherry, mahogany, oak, and poplar),
with gilt-brass paw toe caps and castors, strings for the lyres,
and gilt-brass and ormolu mounts, 28 1/2 in. high, 35 in. wide,
17 1/2 in. deep (at the top), 18 in. deep (at the castors);
open: 35 x 35 in.

Although many major pieces of American Neo-Classical furniture can now be authoritatively assigned to the likes of Duncan Phyfe, Charles-Honoré Lannuier, Thomas Seymour, and Isaac Vose, other pieces of equal distinction have defied attribution. A case in point is this card table, which is part of a group of card tables, work tables, and a single drop-leaf table that Henry Hawley, formerly Chief Curator of Later Western Art at the Cleveland Museum of Art, brought together in an article in the January 1988 issue of *The Bulletin of The Cleveland Museum of Art*.

Although it has long been acknowledged that the pieces in this group were made in Philadelphia, Hawley noted that one of the work tables actually bears a fragment of a maker's label, which reads only "Philadelphie, Pa.," surely indicating that the cabinetmaker who made it was one of the many French émigrés who had arrived in the city in the early years of the nineteenth century. In conjunction with a related work table in the collection of the Philadelphia Museum of Art that he borrowed for *Classical America* in 1963 (pp. 43 no. 20 illus., 76 no. 20), Berry Tracy suggested that it was "possibly by Michel Bouvier, Philadelphia, ca. 1815–1820." Although little is known of Bouvier's life and work, we do know that he fled France in the wake of Napoleon's defeat at Waterloo, and arrived in New York in August 1815. He apparently remained there until sometime in 1817 when he took up residence in Philadelphia. Perhaps not coincidentally, the present table dates to just that moment.

In his article, Hawley suggested that Bouvier may actually have been engaged in the cabinetmaking trade in New York during this period, "perhaps in the shop of his [French] compatriot Charles-Honoré Lannuier" (p. 21). Hawley further postulated that a possible association with Lannuier might explain the strong parallels between Lannuier's work and this group of Philadelphia tables, especially the mutual use of exotically figured light-colored woods and some of the same ormolu mounts. For just as striped maple and bird's eye maple make important aesthetic contributions to the success of the Philadelphia tables, so, too, did Lannuier use bird's eye maple to considerable effect on a remarkable pair of figural card tables now divided between The Metropolitan Museum of Art and the collection of Linda and George Kaufman (Kenny et al., *Honoré Lannuier*, pp. 93 plate 43, 212 nos. 83 and 84, respectively), and a pier table that generously employs a richly figured burl elm (ibid., pp. 55 plate 21, 218 no. 102). This might also account for a mutual use of certain ormolu mounts, the one on the center of the skirt of the present table and the mount on the platform supporting the lyre both appearing on pieces of Lannuier furniture as well, but very rarely on other pieces of American furniture of this period.

One other possible relationship between the present table and New York production is the unique presence on this table of water-leaf carving on the upper reaches of the four saber legs, a signature feature of many works by Duncan Phyfe, but also seen on such pieces by Lannuier as a marble-top stand (Kenny et al., *Honoré Lannuier*, p. 135 plate 68), the Bosley chairs (ibid., p. 134 plate 59), and various card tables (for example, ibid., p. 132 plate 58).

Thus, although this table is still assigned to Philadelphia based on the fragment of a label on a related piece, it is possible that it was actually made in New York by Bouvier or another French cabinetmaker who ultimately settled in Philadelphia.

4

Attributed to

DUNCAN PHYFE

1770–1854

New York (active 1794–1847)

Secrétaire à Abattant, about 1820

Mahogany, rosewood, and striped maple (secondary woods: mahogany and pine), with ormolu mounts, gilt brass, marble, glass, and tooled and gilded leather, 64 in. high, 37¾ in. wide, 21⅜ in. deep; 40⅝ in. deep (with desk open)

Whereas the tall chest, or "highboy," was the signature piece of American case furniture made during the succession of eighteenth-century styles, so the *secrétaire à abattant* was the most significant form of case furniture made in the Neo-Classical period.

The present *secrétaire* was made in New York about 1820, almost certainly in the workshop of Duncan Phyfe, and displays an ultimate level of design and craft characteristic of the best production of the Phyfe shop.

Just as one can trace the evolution of Phyfe chair design from the delicate reeded English Regency-inspired chairs of the 1810s to the simple *chaises gondoles* (cat. 9) that the shop produced for such clients as Samuel A. Foot (1790–1872) and John Laurence Manning (1816–1889) in the late 1830s and early 1840s, there is a parallel stylistic sequence for the *secrétaires à abattants* that the Phyfe shop produced between about 1818–20 and the early 1840s. Perhaps the earliest of the Phyfe pieces in this group is a *secrétaire* that likely dates to around 1818–20 (Kenny et al., *Duncan Phyfe*, pp. 214–15 plate 37), which was for a while an ornament of Decatur House in Washington, D.C. Subsequent to that example is one that was formerly in the collection of Hirschl & Adler Galleries and later in the Jack Warner Collection of Gulf States Paper, Tuscaloosa, Alabama, during which time it was shown at The Metropolitan Museum as a collateral piece in the Lannuier exhibition (see Kenny et al., *Honoré Lannuier*, p. 92 fig. 49). Contemporaneous with that piece is one now in a New York private collection, which was curiously published by Robert C. Smith in one of his series of articles on

Anthony G. Quervelle in *The Magazine Antiques* ([January 1974], p. 181). A few other examples of the form have appeared that also date to the early 1820s, but by the 1830s Phyfe's *secrétaires à abattants* took on the same more architectonic character as the other forms being produced by his shop at the time.

The earliest *secrétaire* of this new style was probably an example formerly with Hirschl & Adler Galleries, which is now in the collection of the Virginia Museum of Fine Arts, Richmond (Kenny et al., *Duncan Phyfe*, p. 232 fig. 1). Still made of rosewood and detailed with a profusion of die-stamped brass inlay seen in the former Decatur *secrétaire*, the piece otherwise follows the tenets of the so-called "Grecian plain style" à la the Foot and Manning commissions. And the final stage in the development of the form is exemplified by two identical mahogany examples, one in the collection of The Metropolitan Museum of Art (Kenny et al., *Duncan Phyfe*, pp. 230–32, plate 45), and one in a New York private collection, on which there are but a few ormolu mounts in the interior, no brass line or die-stamped inlay, or gilding, but the remarkably figured mahogany veneers themselves became the dominant decorative feature.

Although made of mahogany instead of rosewood, the present *secrétaire* fits comfortably in the midst of this development. In form, it is extremely close to the former Decatur secretary, including the arched cove, full-length free-standing columns with ormolu capitals and bases, and paw feet of identical design.

5

Attributed to

DUNCAN PHYFE

1770–1854

New York (active 1794–1847)

Box Sofa, about 1818–20

Rosewood, and mahogany (feet), partially paint-grained rosewood and gilded (secondary woods: ash and black cherry), with ormolu mounts, die-stamped brass inlay inset with rosewood, brass line inlay, gilt-brass sabots and castors, and upholstery, 33¾ in. high, 82 in. long, 27¼ in. deep

One of the handsomest forms of furniture produced in the United States during the 1820s and perhaps into the 1830s was the so-called "box sofa," named either for its box-like form or for the fact that its seat is often upholstered over a separate frame made like a large slip seat. These sofas all appear to be of New York origin, and relate stylistically to a group of sideboards, cellarettes, and various card and center tables that represent a blend of French Restauration and English Regency designs. Indeed, the prototype for the form of these sofas may be a group of three designs for a "library sofa" reproduced by George Smith as Plate 60 in his *A Collection of Designs for Household Furniture and Interior Decoration in the Most Approved and Elegant Taste*, which was published surprisingly early in 1808 by J. Taylor of 59 High Holborn, London, including plates that he had designed when he was at 38 High Holborn in 1805. The accompanying text notes that the "Three Designs for Sofas [are] intended for Libraries" and suggests that "the frames ... should be of mahogany." Not surprisingly, all of the examples that have appeared have been made of mahogany—save for this example and an identical sofa in the collection of the Art Institute of Chicago (Feld and Feld, *Of the Newest Fashion*, pp. 50 illus. in color, 51, 92 cat. 17), both of which are executed in rosewood. Both of these are also enriched with French ormolu mounts of the best quality in patterns that appear on other pieces associated with the shop of Duncan Phyfe, brass

line and die-stamped brass inlay inset with rosewood, and other decorative features that place them in a unique class, and also suggest that they pre-date most or all of the other known examples of the form, possibly even pushing them back into the late 1810s. Cabinetmakers of the first rank rarely made duplicates except as pairs, and since the Hirschl & Adler and Art Institute of Chicago sofas are identical, it is very likely that they were initially conceived of as a pair.

Although many of the mahogany sofas of this form have been ascribed to Phyfe, a considerable variation in design and workmanship suggests that others were also making pieces of this design. On the other hand, the quality of this sofa and the one in Chicago far surpasses that of the extant mahogany examples and can be ranked, qualitatively and stylistically, with the exceptional furniture that Duncan Phyfe was making for Thomas Donaldson (Kenny et al., *Duncan Phyfe*, pp. 208–13 plates 32–36), and others in the years bracketing 1820.

This sofa is embellished with beautifully turned and carved feet that are variously gilded and paint-grained rosewood, unusually elaborate die-rolled gilt-brass, sabots, and castors, French ormolu capitals and bases on the flanking columns, and a suite of three ormolu mounts in two patterns across the front seat rail.

Attributed to

DUNCAN PHYFE

1770–1854

New York (active 1794–1847)

Pier Table, about 1817–22

Rosewood, with maple [probably] feet painted *verde antique* and gilded (secondary woods: tulip poplar), with die-stamped brass inlay inset with rosewood, ormolu mounts, marble, and mirror plate, 36¼ in. high, 42¼ in. wide, 18⅛ in. deep (overall)

Pier tables were undoubtedly the most popular form of furniture made in the United States during the Neo-Classical period. Their popularity and utility is certainly confirmed by the considerable number of examples that have survived, which represent the entire spectrum from elaborate productions by the French emigré cabinetmaker Charles-Honoré Lannuier, and those of equal quality and complexity by Duncan Phyfe, to very ordinary, vernacular examples that signal the mass-produced furniture that was shortly to fill houses across America.

Although today we recognize such pieces as the present table as distinctive works by Phyfe, its lavish use of the finest French ormolu mounts, two different patterns of die-stamped brass inlaid with rosewood, superb quality Brazilian rosewood veneers, and marble columns, pilasters, and top, all closely parallel the contemporaneous work of Lannuier, and for many years the work of New York's two greatest cabinetmakers of the early nineteenth century was often confused. The Metropolitan Museum's monographic exhibitions of the work of Lannuier in 1998 and Phyfe in 2011 were important steps in beginning to clarify their individual styles.

This table is closely related to an example in a private collection in New York (Kenny et al., *Duncan Phyfe*, pp. 216–17 plate 38), and its original mate in the collection of The Metropolitan Museum (Feld and Feld, *The World of Duncan Phyfe*, pp. 48–49 no. 20 illus.). Those tables and the present table may vary in the patterns of the feet and in the selection of the ormolu mounts and die-stamped borders, but this is a function of a desire to produce individualized works for different clients, as duplicates were rarely made except as original pairs. Here, in place of the familiar paw feet on The Metropolitan table and its original companion, Phyfe has used a turned foot with carved and gilded lotus leaves against a background in *verde antique*, which was meant to simulate the color of excavated bronze.

9

Attributed to

D U N C A N   P H Y F E

1 7 7 0 – 1 8 5 4

New York (active 1794–1847)

Pair Armchairs en Gondole, about 1835–40

Mahogany (secondary woods: ash; slip seats: poplar),
with gilt-brass castors, and upholstery; each 34¾ in. high,
21½ in. wide, 25⅛ in. deep (overall)

Easy chairs—or *fauteuils* and *bergères* as they are variously called
in France—were rarely made in the cabinetmaking centers of
Boston, New York, Philadelphia, and Baltimore in the Neo-Classical
period, and it is thus likely that French and English imports
were most frequently used in American parlors and bedrooms.
There were exceptions, of course, such as a handsome chair made
by Duncan Phyfe for New Yorker Luman Reed (1787–1836)
(Tracy et al., *19th-Century America*, no. 78 illus.); a pair, also by
Phyfe, for Stephen Van Rensselaer III (Kenny et al., *Duncan Phyfe*,
p. 141 fig. 182 illus.); and in Philadelphia, a set of large-scale
armchairs produced by Joseph Barry for Isaac Minis of Savannah
(Feld and Feld, *Very Rich and Handsome*, p. 42 no. 15 illus.).

For John Laurence Manning's Millford Plantation, near the
present Pinewood, in Clarendon County, South Carolina, Duncan
Phyfe provided a unique set of fourteen armchairs *en gondole*
for the dining room (Smith, "Living with Antiques," p. 737 plate
IX), and a similar set for the double drawing room (ibid., pp.
732–33 plate II, 736 plate VIII). Both sets of chairs have cabriole
legs in the front and sharply raked legs at the back that are like
those on boldly designed klismos chairs of the 1820s and 1830s.
The two sets of chairs differ essentially in the curved crestrails
of the dining chairs and the slightly peaked profile of those in the
drawing room.

The present pair of chairs is distinctly related to the Millford
chairs. The general form is the same, the back being finished
with the same pointed profile as the drawing room chairs.
In place of the cabriole front legs of both sets of Millford chairs,
here the front legs are straight and turned, and the back legs,
still dramatically drawn, are now of a cabriole form.

The Millford chairs are documented by a bill of lading for
a furniture delivery to Charleston in June 1841, so it is likely
the Millford furniture was produced between Manning's apparent
visit to Phyfe's shop in October 1840 and June 1841.
Thus, the present chairs, which are also similar in style to the
furniture Phyfe produced for Samuel A. Foot's residence at 678
Broadway, New York in 1837 (Tracy et al., *19th-Century America*,
no. 79 illus.), probably date sometime between the later
1830s and the early 1840s.

Like the Manning and Foot chairs, and other pieces documented
as by Phyfe, the outsides of the scrolled arms of these
chairs are finished with very flat turned mahogany rosettes with
crisply molded edges, a detail that, with its ultimate finesse, appears
to be unique to Phyfe.

10

Attributed to

THOMAS SEYMOUR

1772–1848

Boston (active alone, 1804–16)

Work Table in the Sheraton Taste, about 1810

Mahogany, striped and bird's eye maple, and ebony
(secondary woods: ash and mahogany), with gilt-brass drawer knobs,
and fabric work bag, 27¾ in. high, 19¼ in. wide, 15¾ in. deep

During the later years of the eighteenth century and the first years of the nineteenth, the appearance of the London publication of Thomas Sheraton's *The Cabinet Maker's and Upholsterer's Drawing Book* in 1796, *The Cabinet Dictionary* in 1803, and his *The Cabinet Maker, Upholsterer and General Artist's Encyclopedia* in 1805, as well as George Hepplewhite's *The Cabinet Maker and Upholsterer's Guide*, which appeared in editions published in 1788, 1789, and 1790, suddenly transformed the aesthetic of high-style furniture made in the United States.

The evolution in style, together with the emergence of the work table as a popular—and important—new form of furniture, resulted in the appearance of a piece that often served the various purposes of sewing, letter writing, and a variety of other female pursuits. Sheraton referred to tables of this form as sewing, or "pouch," tables to provide ladies with an alternative place to store their needlework and tools instead of in pockets or under skirts.

The present table, first published in 1959 by Vernon C. Stoneman in his book *John and Thomas Seymour* (p. 242 no. 155 illus.), was certainly made in Boston in the years bracketing 1810, and was likely a product of the distinguished cabinetmaking shop of Thomas Seymour, who was the leading designer and maker of furniture in Boston at the time.

The framework of the table is executed in mahogany, which is enhanced by inlays of brilliantly figured striped and bird's eye maple, all banded in extremely fine borders of ebony. This, plus the perfect serpentine profile of all four sides and the beautifully turned and reeded legs, contribute to a piece of ultimate quality and distinction.

A nearly identical example is in the collection of the Museum of Fine Arts, Boston (acc. no. 1984.738).

11

THOMAS SEYMOUR

1772–1848

with

THOMAS WIGHTMAN

1759–1827

as carver

Boston

Pier Table with Carved Tablet, about 1805–10

Mahogany (secondary woods: cherry and mahogany), with
gilt brass and marble, 35¼ in. high, 55 in. wide, 26½ in. deep

Inscribed (on underside of marble top): Joel Koopman /
18 Beacon Street/ Boston Mass.

This pier, or console, table by Thomas Seymour ranks as one of
the great masterpieces of American furniture from the first
decade of the nineteenth century. It was closely based upon engraved Plate 63 in Thomas Sheraton's *The Cabinet Directory*
(fig. 6), which was published in London in 1803, and which Seymour acquired, as Robert Mussey writes, "as early as 1804
when he opened his influential Boston Furniture Warehouse…
or it might have been acquired as late as 1808 when he began
making a large group of London-style furniture for style-maven
Elizabeth Derby" (essay by Robert D. Mussey, November 2009,
copy in Hirschl & Adler archives). Seymour's own copy of the
book, bearing his signature, is in the collection of the Museum
of Fine Arts, Boston.

Various elements of the upright supports of the table are all
contained in the Sheraton illustration: the "capitals," the feet,
and the reeded columns, etc., but their arrangement and spacing
varies. The shape of the lower shelf is the same, and the back
and sides of the shelf are ornamented with a die-stamped gilt-

FIG. 6

Thomas Sheraton
The Cabinet Directory (1803)
plate 63

brass gallery, although the scale seems larger in the Sheraton plate than on the table itself. Both the Sheraton design and the Seymour table have marble tops.

The considerable success of this table owes as much to the talent of carver Thomas Wightman as it does to Seymour's fine adaptation of Sheraton's design. Born in Liverpool, England, and trained as a carver in London, where he worked from 1780 to 1797, Whitman emigrated to the United States with his growing family in 1797. He seems to have worked first for John Seymour, Thomas Seymour's father, and then for Thomas himself until Thomas closed his own shop in 1817. Meanwhile, he was also doing work for the cabinetmaking firm of Vose & Coates, and continued to work for Isaac Vose when Seymour joined the firm in 1819. His crisp carvings are easily identifiable, but the presence of his carving on a piece of furniture does not confirm an attribution to one or both of the Seymours, as he is also documented as having worked for others in the cabinetmaking trade in Boston.

There are three other console tables by Seymour of essentially the same design. A pair made for Elizabeth Derby West of Salem, Massachusetts, which retain their original inlaid wooden tops, is now in the collection of the Museum of Fine Arts, Boston (Mussey, *Furniture Masterworks*, pp. 282–83 no. 74 illus.). A single table, now considerably altered and with a replaced wooden top, is at Gore Place, Waltham, Massachusetts (photograph in Hirschl & Adler archives). The present table has survived in excellent condition including its original marble top (fig. 7).

All four tables are a further demonstration of the successful partnership of Seymour as designer and Thomas Wightman as carver, as the quality of Wightman's contribution helped to establish Seymour's shop as one without peer in Federal Boston.

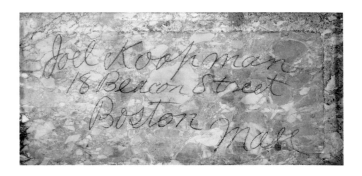

FIG. 7

Thomas Seymour
Pier Table, detail of the underside of the marble top
Like many other original marble tops on Boston pier tables and *secrétaires à abattant*s of the Neo-Classical period, the marble, as made, was reduced in thickness around the perimeter, but remained at full thickness at the center. This became a hallmark of Boston production in this period.

Attributed to

ISAAC VOSE & SON

(active 1819–25)

with

THOMAS SEYMOUR

1772–1848

as foreman (active in the Vose Shop, 1819–25)

Boston

Work Table, about 1819–24

Rosewood (secondary woods: ash, mahogany, pine, and Spanish cedar), with die-rolled gilt-brass moldings filled with lead, ormolu mounts, steel castors, and fabric work bag, 29½ in. high, 23 in. wide, 17¼ in. deep

Without question, Isaac Vose, with his association first with Joshua Coates (active 1815–19) and later with his son, Isaac, Jr., and Thomas Seymour (active 1819–25), produced a stunning array of furniture in the Neo-Classical taste, varying from a delicate interpretation of the style of Londoner George Hepplewhite (1727–1786) to a perfect blend of French Empire and English Regency designs.

This newly discovered work table is exemplary of their signature style in the years around 1820, showcasing fine rosewood veneers, French ormolu mounts, and English die-rolled moldings, together with a flawless sense of scale and composition to create an object that stands at the summit of their production.

The table is one of four of its general type that have appeared. One, with drop leaves and a trestle base, was included in the 2018 exhibition *Rather Elegant Than Showy: The Classical Furniture of Isaac Vose*, at the Massachusetts Historical Society, Boston (Mussey and Pearce, pp. XIV and 236 fig. 277); another nearly identical example in a private collection; a third table of slightly huskier scale, also privately owned, that has forsaken drop leaves in favor of canted corners, and features typical bun

feet characteristic of Boston production of this period; and the present table, also with canted corners and bun feet.

All four tables feature both French ormolu mounts of excellent quality and a profusion of English gilt-brass beaded moldings, the present table with an unusually elaborate program of eighteen ormolu mounts and many feet of the beaded brass molding.

13

THOMAS SEYMOUR

1772–1848

for

ISAAC VOSE & SON

(active 1819–25)

with

THOMAS WIGHTMAN

1759–1827

as carver (active in the Vose Shop, 1819–25)

Boston

Pair Klismos-form Side Chairs, about 1815–20

Mahogany (secondary woods: maple; slip seats: ash),
with upholstered slip seats; each, 33½ in. high, 19⅜ in. wide,
20½ in. deep (overall)

Inscribed (with punch, on one chair): XIII [crossed out] / VII
[slip seat]; (on the second chair): V [chair] / I [slip seat]

The symbiotic relationship that developed between Thomas Seymour and his master carver Thomas Wightman is nowhere more perfectly expressed than in this pair of side chairs. As Robert Mussey and Clark Pearce have noted ("Classical Excellence," p. 277), Seymour produced at least eight variations of this model (for example, see Tracy et al., *19th-Century America*, no. 30 illus.; Talbott, "Boston Empire Furniture—Part I," p. 887 fig. 12; Talbott, "Seating Furniture in Boston, 1810–1835," pp. 964–65 plate XII; and Mussey and Pearce, "Classical Excellence," p. 277 fig. 39), of which none are more elaborate than the present pair.

Unusually generous in scale within the range of Boston klismos chairs, they feature boldly reeded stiles that flow into the top of the siderails and down the front of the legs. The complex and beautifully articulated crestrails feature a large rectangular tablet at the center, which is carved with acanthus leaves. And the beautifully articulated backsplat, below, once again has a carved central panel, with additional leafy carvings on each side. The carved paw feet, which represent an embellishment seen on only a few chairs in this group, are an added refinement that contributes significantly to the poetic stance of the chairs.

These chairs are undoubtedly from the same set as an armchair included by Mussey and Pearce in their exhibition, *Rather Elegant than Showy: The Classical Furniture of Isaac Vose*, and published in the accompanying catalogue (pp. 124 fig. 138, 263 fig. 327, 265). In a chapter titled "By These Signs You Will Know Them: Connoisseurship & Construction of Vose Furniture," Pearce describes a "quirky little wedge-shaped shelf" at the proper left and right rear corners of the interior of the seat frame, a detail present in these chairs as well, "which opens a window into the complexity and meticulousness of Seymour's work" and provides another compelling detail to confirm an attribution to the Vose shop under Seymour's supervision.

14

Attributed to

THOMAS SEYMOUR

1772–1848

(active in the Vose Shop, 1819–25)

possibly for

ISAAC VOSE

Boston

Cumberland-action Dining Table, about 1815–20

Mahogany (secondary woods: pine and poplar), with gilt-brass toe-caps and castors, 28¾ in. high, 62¼ in. long, 60 in. wide; 60 in. long, 17 in. wide (with leaves down)

The most popular form of dining table made in Boston during the first quarter of the nineteenth century was the so-called "Cumberland-action" table, which was essentially a drop-leaf table that was extended by moving the supports to 45-degree angles at each of the four corners. The name of the table is said to have been derived from a table of this form made in England for Henry Frederick, Duke of Cumberland.

The present table consists of a single section, but, occasionally, two- or three-section "banquet" tables were produced.

A two-section table of this design bears the label of Thomas Constantine of New York (private collection; see Feld and Feld, *The World of Duncan Phyfe*, pp. 32–33 no. 11 illus.), but Thomas Seymour scholar Robert D. Mussey, Jr., has observed that the various tables of this form are "so similar in construction and detailing that they must have been produced by one shop, probably that of Thomas Seymour" (Mussey, *Furniture Masterworks*, p. 327). (The table labeled by Constantine is now thought to have been made by Seymour and subsequently retailed or restored by Constantine in New York.)

Seymour made tables of this design from the days when he operated his own business until the closure of the Vose shop in 1825, and possibly beyond. The earliest tables of this design probably had upright supports with ring turnings to create a bamboo-like effect, while those with vertical reeds, such as the present example, probably date from the early years of his association with Vose. The latest examples are likely those in which the reeds are swirled, some of which may postdate Seymour's years in the Vose shop.

15

Attributed to

THOMAS SEYMOUR

1 7 7 2 – 1 8 4 8

working for

JAMES BARKER

(active together, 1817–19)

or

ISAAC VOSE & SON

(active 1819–25)

with

THOMAS WIGHTMAN

1 7 5 9 – 1 8 2 7

as carver (active in the Vose Shop, 1819–25)

Boston

Pier Table, about 1818–20

Mahogany (secondary woods: chestnut and pine), with marble and mirror plate, 36 in. high, 50³⁄₄ in. wide, 21⁵⁄₈ in. deep

The research on the various incarnations of Isaac Vose in the cabinetmaking business in Boston undertaken by Robert D. Mussey, Jr., and Clark Pearce ("Classical Excellence," pp. 250ff.; and the catalogue of the 2018 exhibition *Rather Elegant Than Showy: The Classical Furniture of Isaac Vose*) has been extremely revealing with respect to the range and quality of the production of the Vose shop, and, concomitantly, the later work of Thomas Seymour, who served as foreman of the Vose shop from 1819 to 1825.

Mussey and Pearce reproduce a silhouette ("Classical Excellence," p. 271 fig. 30) by Auguste Edouart (1789–1861), here illustrated as fig. 8, of members of the Daniel P. Parker family, who are set against a sepia wash background detailing the parlor in their Alexander Parris-designed rowhouse at 40 Beacon Street, Boston. At the center of the interior is what they describe as "a Grecian center table," which has a drawer fitted out as a desk, a piece which is not now known but which is extremely similar to a center table that they illustrate ("Classical Excellence," p. 271 fig. 31; and Mussey and Pearce, *Rather Elegant*, pp. 130 fig. 148, 219 fig. 237), and that they attribute to Sey-

FIG. 8

Augustin-Amant-Constant Fidèle Edouart (1789–1861)
The Daniel P. Parker Family in the Front Parlor of their Home at 40 Beacon Street, Boston, 1842
Free-hand cut black paper detailed with graphite pencil drawing, mounted on a ground of sepia wash and Chinese white, 18¹⁄₁₆ x 30 in.

Private collection

mour, either working for James Barker or Isaac Vose, about 1818–20, except that the latter table has probably never had a platform like that of the table shown by Edouart, and is not outfitted with a desk drawer.

The present pier table is so close in detail to the Vose center table and to the one shown in the Parker silhouette that it is possible that some or all may originally have been made *en suite* as part of a single commission. Although nothing is known of the early ownership of this pier table, it appears to be very close in detail to the table shown on the curved wall at the left side of the Parker silhouette. Like the Parker pier table, this table has an incurvate front. Further, the original top of a green variegated mar-

ble was originally curved at the back, confirming that it either sat in the curved bay fronting the Parker home, or in another similar setting in a Boston townhouse or elsewhere, possibly that of Nathan Appleton, who lived in an identical adjoining Parris townhouse and who owned a matching side table, or sideboard in current usage (Mussey and Pearce, *Rather Elegant*, p. 107 fig. 119).

The quatrefoils at the center and ends of the skirt, which again relate to those on the center table in the Vose exhibition and to those on the Appleton table, foreshadow the onset of the Gothic Revival, which within a decade was to become a significant addition to the eclectic, revivalist aesthetic of early nineteenth-century taste.

16

Attributed to

ISAAC VOSE & SON

(active 1819–25)

with

THOMAS SEYMOUR

1772–1848

as foreman (active in the Vose Shop, 1819–25)

Boston

Set of Twelve Klismos-form Side Chairs, about 1822–24

Mahogany (secondary woods: birch; slip seats: poplar),
with upholstered slip seats; each, 34 in. high, 18 13/16 in. wide,
23 1/8 in. deep (overall)

Boldly profiled klismos chairs, ultimately inspired by examples depicted on ancient Greek vase paintings and burial stele and disseminated broadly through illustrations in such books as Thomas Hope's *Household Furniture and Interior Decoration* (1807) and George Smith's *A Collection of Designs for Household Furniture and Interior Decoration in the Most Approved and Elegant Taste* (1806–08), were a staple of Boston production in the years after 1815. Many variations of the klismos form were produced, but none were more dramatic in design than those of this set, where a combination of the sharply curved profile of the stiles flanking the back, and the dramatic rake of the front and rear legs served to set them apart from more conventional examples.

This set of chairs is identical to another set of twelve that descended in the Higginson family of Boston (fig. 9), as well as a few singles and pairs in such collections as that of Linda and George Kaufman (Flanigan, pp. 140–41 no. 51 illus.); the Henry Francis du Pont Winterthur Museum, Winterthur, Delaware (Talbott, "Seating Furniture," p. 960 plate VI); and The White House, Washington, D.C.

After discussing an armchair that likely belonged to the same set as those discussed and illustrated as cat. 8 in this cata-

logue, Clark Pearce writes, in a chapter aptly titled "By These Signs You Will Know Them: Connoisseurship & Construction of Vose Furniture" in *Rather Elegant Than Showy*, that "around 1823...Seymour seems to have expanded his repertoire with different chair styles." He continues: "These followed a similar Klismos form, but had tablet crestrails that extended *beyond* the stiles.... Most often these chairs had stayrails that imitated variations of drapery supported in the corners by half anthemia" (p. 267). And in this context he illustrates a chair identical to those in the present set (fig. 338 on p. 268).

This set of chairs descended in the Fales family of Boston and were almost certainly made for the wealthy merchant Samuel Fales (1775–1848) for use in his residence at 171 (later 174) Colonnade Row, a London-inspired composition of attached townhouses built in 1810–12 from the design of Charles Bulfinch (1763–1844) on a stretch of Common Street between Mason Street on the south and West Street on the north. Fales descendent DeCoursey Fales later described the setting as "a block which was then, and for many years afterwards, the most aristocratic place of residence in Boston" (Fales, p. 90).

FIG. 9

Attributed to Isaac Vose & Son,
with Thomas Seymour as foreman, Boston
*One of a Set of Twelve Klismos-form Side Chairs
from the Higginson Family*, about 1822–24
Mahogany, 32 1/2 in. high

Private Collection

17

BOSTON

Seven-drawer Tall Chest, about 1825

Mahogany (secondary woods: mahogany, pine, and poplar), 45⅝ in. high, 27⅝ in. wide, 14⅝ in. deep

Inscribed (on six drawer locks): SECURE; (on seventh lock): CHUBB'S / PATENT / 57 ST PAULS CHY / LONDON / CHUBB & SON / MAKERS TO / HER MAJESTY / 632284; (on one hinge): [BUR?]NE PATENT; (on master lock): 2 LEVER

Although some Boston furniture of the Neo-Classical period is elaborately decorated with ormolu mounts, brass moldings, and carved and gilded elements (for example, the work table attributed to Isaac Vose & Son, cat. 12), other pieces are simpler and are said to reflect the "conservative" taste of many of Boston's great families. The simplicity evident in these pieces is not an indication of a less-expensive line of furniture or a less-sophisticated patronage, but, like the so-called "Grecian plain style" of Duncan Phyfe's furniture in the later 1830s and into the 1840s, is, instead, a reflection of a new aesthetic that evolved from a parallel stylistic evolution among English and French cabinetmakers beginning in the late 1820s.

In this seven-drawer chest, the focus is on the selection of the finest mahogany veneers, the grain of the wood becoming the principal decorative device. And if the added flourishes of ormolu and gilt-brass mounts have been forsaken, so, too, have gilt-brass drawer pulls, the seven drawers here equipped with their original beautifully turned mahogany knobs, which are characteristic of Boston production of this period.

As a form, the seven-drawer chest is a standard item among English and French cabinetmakers, both those working earlier and later, but it appears to be otherwise unknown among the production of Boston Neo-Classical cabinetmakers.

In the present example, a hinged vertical mahogany strip running the full height at the right can be locked in order to secure the contents of all of the drawers, each of which is also supplied with its own lock. One of the locks was supplied by Chubb & Son, who opened a workshop on Temple Street in the West Midlands industrial town of Wolverhampton, England, in 1818. Two years later, in 1820, they opened a shop at 57 St. Paul's Churchyard in London, which establishes a *terminus post quem* for this chest.

18A

Attributed to

THOMAS S. RENSHAW

&

JOHN BARNHART

Baltimore (active about 1814–15)

Painted Chinese Red and Gilded "Fancy" Side Chair, about 1815

Mahogany, painted and gilded, with caning, 32½ in. high, 19 in. wide, 21 in. deep (overall)

These two chairs represent two distinctive phases in the evolution of Neo-Classical design, just as the two banjo clocks (cats. 20A and 20B) and the two pairs of wall brackets (cats. 19A and 19B) show the stylistic changes that took place in a ten-to-twenty-year period.

Although painted furniture of ultimate sophistication was made in virtually all of the major cabinetmaking centers in Federal America, no city produced more or better work in this genre than Baltimore. Much painted furniture produced there has been ascribed to the firm of John and Hugh Finlay, who early in their career received a commission for a set of thirty-six painted chairs, four settees, and two sofas for the Oval Room of The White House, Washington, D.C., all of which were destroyed in the burning of that building in 1814. From the same period is this chair with the Chinese-red background

18B

Attributed to

JOHN FINLAY

1777–1851

&

HUGH FINLAY

1781–1831

Baltimore (active about 1800/01–30)

Painted Black and Gilded "Fancy" Side Chair, about 1830

Poplar, painted and gilded (secondary woods: pine and poplar), with die-stamped gilt-brass rosettes, caning, and original red moreen fabric [beneath replacement fabric on rondel], 33¾ in. high, 18⅝ in. wide, 23¾ in. deep (overall)

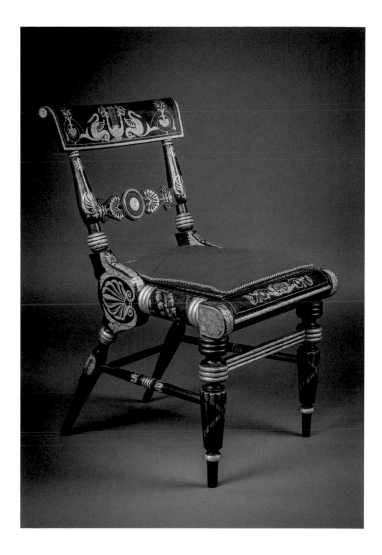

(cat. 18A), which is from the same set as one previously published in the catalogue of the Hirschl & Adler exhibition, *Very Rich and Handsome* (pp. 68–69 no. 32 illus.). The chairs are attributed to the Baltimore firm of Renshaw and Barnhart on the basis of a signed settee of related design and decoration in the collection of the Baltimore Museum of Art (Elder, pp. 42–45 no. 20). Of the partnership, Renshaw was the cabinetmaker and Barnhart was the "ornamenter," or painter.

Despite the sophistication of their work, including here a dramatic Chinese-red background, and the use of painted "shadows" that articulate three separate planes, their partnership was apparently unable to survive the powerful competition of the Finlay firm.

Indeed, the Finlays' business survived into the 1830s, along the way producing a legendary range of painted furniture that was unsurpassed in its time. Among their most dramatic works is a set of chairs, likely numbering at least twenty-four based upon the incised number of XXII on the seat of the black chair (cat. 18B). The unusual design, termed a "wheel back" in Baltimore vernacular, appears to have been based on an ancient Roman folding chair, which had a hinge at the circular area

at the back to facilitate the folding of the chair for easy transportation.

The decoration of the present chair partakes of many of the same motifs seen on other pieces ascribed to the Finlays. Although Hugh Finlay is referred to in contemporary accounts as a gifted painter, there is also evidence that the Baltimore artist Cornelius de Beet (1772–1840) may have been responsible for the painted decoration on some of the Finlays' furniture (ibid., pp. 12–13).

The red moreen squab on the chair is based upon the apparently unique survival of a nearly identical fabric on the rondel in the center of the backsplat, now reversibly covered with a piece of modern red moreen.

19 A

AMERICAN

Pair Eagle Wall Brackets, about 1820

Pine and spruce, gessoed and gilded,
14³/₈ in. high, 14⁵/₈ in. wide, 9⁷/₈ in. deep

Like carved and gilded candle sconces, which were often topped by gilded or ebonized eagles, wall brackets were a staple of early nineteenth-century production. Many were made in England, fewer in the United States. The present pair of brackets with opposing eagles (cat. 19A) was made in America and likely dates to about 1820 when American Neo-Classical furniture was richly ornamented and architectural settings had become correspondingly more elaborate.

By contrast, the simpler pair of brackets (cat. 19B), also of American origin and probably dating to the 1830s, represents a newer aesthetic, when temple-form houses sprinkled the countryside and simple row houses proliferated in cities. Stylistically, the brackets parallel the more abstract, so-called "Grecian plain style" furniture that Duncan Phyfe made for Samuel Foot's new residence at 678 Broadway, New York (Tracy et al., *19th-Century America*, no. 79; and Kenny et al., *Duncan Phyfe*, pp. 233–35 plates 46 and 47), and for John Laurence Manning's Greek Revival Millford Plantation in rural Pinewood, South Carolina (Smith, "Living with Antiques," pp. 732–41).

19 B

AMERICAN

Pair Wall Brackets, 1830s

Pine, gessoed and gilded,
11 in. high, 11 5/16 in. wide, 8 in. deep

20A

SIMON WILLARD

1753–1848

Roxbury, Massachusetts (active early 1780s–1823)

Banjo Clock (The "Improved Timepiece"), about 1805

Wood, gessoed and partially gilded and painted white, with *églomisé* glass panels, brass, painted dial, glass, and clock mechanism, 42⅞ in. high, 10⅞ in. wide, 5⅝ in. deep

Signed and inscribed (in gold, on the lower glass panel):
S. WILLARD'S PATENT

One of the household names in the pantheon of American artists of the past is that of Simon Willard, whose name is as familiar as those of many of our leading American artists and craftsmen. Maker of tall-case ("grandfather") clocks, thirty-hour Grafton wall clocks, shelf clocks, improved timepieces ("banjo") clocks, and patent alarm ("lighthouse") clocks, Willard was a member of a large family of clockmakers. His mature years were spent in Roxbury, Massachusetts, a suburb of Boston, where he received a patent in 1802 for his "improved timepiece," known today as a "Banjo Clock," which was, as Willard historians Dr. Roger W. Robinson and Herschel B. Burt have written, "a significant improvement over the thirty-hour wall clock as it only had to be wound once a week" (p. 11).

A review of the account books of Willard's Roxbury neighbor John Doggett (1780–1857), who was a noted frame and mirror maker, has confirmed an important working relationship between them. Clearly, Doggett supplied Willard with some—possibly all—of the components of his clocks, likely including the cases themselves. For example, between 1804 and 1809, the period in which the painted and gilded clock (cat. 20A) was made, Doggett billed Willard for more than eighty brackets, or "pedestals," for his "timepieces," at prices ranging from $3.25 to $4.00 for pedestals without balls and $4.50 for those with balls, as seen in this example. Doggett also billed $0.75 for gilding "small" eagles, likely for use as the finials on Willard's clocks, which were pos-

sibly supplied by Salem carver Samuel McIntire (1757–1811), as those like that atop the present clock follow a design familiar through his larger eagles such as one from the west gate of Washington Square, Salem, Massachusetts (Lahikainen, p. 197 fig. 4-215), and one from the cupola of the Lynn Academy, Lynn, Massachusetts (ibid., p. 199 figs. 4-218A and B), and also smaller examples given to him (fig. 10).

FIG. 10

Samuel McIntire (1757–1811)

Eagle, about 1804–05

Wood, gessoed and gilded, 14 in. high (including base)

Collection of Hirschl & Adler Galleries, New York

The painted white surfaces on the sides of the present clock and others by Willard have led to their description as "bridal clocks," but Paul Foley writes that "there is no conclusive evidence that they were made specifically as wedding gifts" (p. 12). Nonetheless, the so-called "bridal" clocks are among the most beautiful examples produced by Simon Willard. Stylistically, this clock fits perfectly within the aesthetic range of Boston cabinetmaking in the first years of the nineteenth century, as exemplified by the delicate work of John and Thomas Seymour.

In contrast, the case of Willard's later clock (cat. 20B), which bears the signature of "Simon Willard and Son" and can thus be dated to their partnership in the years 1823–26, has moved ahead stylistically and partakes of an aesthetic in tune with the work of Isaac Vose and Son and his association with the later work of Thomas Seymour. Although the template of the case remains the same, the delicate beaded borders surrounding the two glass panels of the gilded case have given way to the simpler, gently rounded profiles of the later clock, the design of the bracket has been simplified, and, in place of the eagle, a turned finial crowns the composition. Additionally, in place of the shiny, gilded surface of the earlier clock, the borders around the glass panels and the bracket have here been ebonized and variously gilded and bronzed in keeping with a type of furniture decoration that became popular in the 1820s.

20 B

SIMON WILLARD & SON

1753–1848

Roxbury, Massachusetts

(active 1823–26)

Banjo Clock (The "Improved Timepiece"), about 1823–26

Mahogany, ebonized, partially stenciled with gold leaf and bronze powder, with *églomisé* glass panels, brass, painted dial, glass, and clock mechanism, 40¼ in. high

Signed and inscribed (on the dial): Simon Willard & Son / No 4378; (on the upper glass panel): PATENT

And the Daughter of Pharoah came down to wash herself at the River—
and when She saw the Ark among the Flags, she sent her maid to fetch it. Exod. Ch. 2 Verse 5th

NEEDLEWORK

21

LYDIA TOWNSEND

at

Mrs. Saunders' and Miss Beach's Academy
Dorchester, Massachusetts

Frame and églomisé *mat probably supplied by*

JOHN DOGGETT

1780–1857

Roxbury, Massachusetts

The Finding of Moses, about 1810

Silk embroidery thread and watercolor on silk, with *églomisé* mat
and gilded frame, 16⅜ x 12⅛ in. (sight size); 20⅝ x 15⅝ in.
(strainer size); 24 x 18⅞ in. (overall, including frame)

Signed and inscribed (with embroidered letters, at bottom of scene):
And the Daughter of Pharoah came down to wash herself at the
River– / and when She saw the Ark among the Flags, she sent her
maid to fetch it Exod. Ch. 2d Verse 5th; (at the bottom of the
églomisé mat): WROUGHT BY LYDIA TOWNSEND / AT MRS.
SAUNDERS & MISS BEACH'S ACADEMY DORCHESTER

Of the various academies that were charged with the instruction
of young ladies in the years bracketing 1800, one of the best was
run by Mrs. Judith Foster Saunders and Miss Clementina Beach
at Dorchester, Massachusetts, a southwestern suburb of Boston.

As early as March 1803, the ladies advertised in the Boston
Columbian Centinel and *The Boston Independent Chronicle* that
they had opened their new school, Clifton Hill Academy, as it
was sometimes called, in a house at the corner of Adams and
East Streets. Although the house had only nine rooms, the 1810
census showed that forty people were residing there, testimony
to their considerable success.

The Academy might easily have slipped into oblivion with
the passage of time, but the extraordinary quality of the needlework created by the students there has given it a reputation far
beyond its day. The subject of the needlework projects undertaken at the Saunders/Beach Academy ranged from the popular
memorials of the day to a departed family member or friend
(cat. 22), to such national worthies as George Washington, and
to biblical and allegorical subjects. Most of the pictorial subjects
were taken from prints, some likely within the pages of the
Academy's library of more than 1,500 volumes.

The subject of the present embroidery is *The Finding of
Moses*. Another embroidery of the same subject, executed by Mary
Crafts at the Saunders/Beach Academy, is in the Winterthur collection (Ring, "Mrs. Saunders' and Miss Beach's Academy," p.
310 fig. 5), and suggests the alternate possibilities that a single
class was assigned a specific subject—in this case The Finding of
Moses—or that the subject was selected by young women at the
school at different times. In both cases, the authorship of the
needlework is proudly proclaimed on the original *églomisé*
mat, Mary Sybil Crafts on the Winterthur example, and Lydia
Townsend on this work.

Whereas the needlework itself was done largely by the students, perhaps with the occasional helping hand of an instructor,
in this case the faces and other anatomical details were probably
executed by Clementina Beach, who is said to have studied with
the eminent portraitist, Gilbert Stuart (1755–1828). Once an
embroidery was finished, it was often sent to John Doggett of
neighboring Roxbury, who would first block it, then "strain" it,
or attach it to a strainer, or a delicate stretcher, supply a glass
which he would decorate with "enameling and lettering," and,
finally, a frame, some of which are identical to that on this embroidery (ibid., p. 303 plates II and III).

The exact identity of Lydia Townsend has not been established. She may have been related to a Dr. Townsend, whose
counsel Mrs. Saunders and Miss Beach sought in purchasing a
house for their Academy. That Dr. Townsend may have been Dr.
David Townsend (1753–1829) of Boston, who fathered seven
children, whose names are not all known to us today.

22

ANN CLAP[P]

at

Mrs. Saunders' and Miss Beach's Academy
Dorchester, Massachusetts

Frame and églomisé *mat probably supplied by*

JOHN DOGGETT

1780–1857

Roxbury, Massachusetts

Memorial to Ebenezer Clap[p], about 1804–07

Silk embroidery thread and watercolor on silk, with *églomisé* mat and gilded frame, 16¾ x 12½ in. (sight size); 20⅜ x 14¾ in. (strainer size); 23⅝ x 18 in. (overall, including frame)

Signed and inscribed (in pencil, at bottom of silk, covered by mat): Wrought by Ann Clap at Mrs. Saunders' and Miss Beach's Academy, Dorchester; (at bottom of *églomisé* mat): WROUGHT by ANN CLAP AT MRS. SAUNDERS & MISS BEACH'S ACADEMY DORCHESTER; (with embroidery, on silk): SACRED / to the MEMORY of / EBENEZER CLAP ESQ^R / who died Jany 29th 1802 Aged 70 / NOT LOST BUT GONE BEFORE

This memorial to Ebenezer Clap[p] (1732–1802) exemplifies the outstanding work in embroidery done at Mrs. Saunders' and Miss Beach's Academy, but, more broadly, is typical of the memorials done variously with embroidery and watercolor, and watercolor alone in the years bracketing 1800.

The memorial was executed by Ann Clap[p] (1792–1868), which is always spelled Clapp in various biographical references, to commemorate the death of her father, Ebenezer Clap[p] on January 29, 1802. Ebenezer, who had lived in a house between Dorchester and Boston, was clearly deserving of his daughter's testimonial. He served as a Colonel in the local Militia, and his rank was later confirmed by the Continental Congress early in 1775. Subsequently, he was active in business, and amassed a considerable amount of real estate, which upon his death resulted in the largest estate probated in neighboring Norfolk County, Massachusetts, up to that time.

This embroidery was probably executed about 1804–07, when Ann Clap[p] was twelve to fifteen years old. Once it was completed, it was likely sent to John Doggett in Roxbury, who supplied a frame identical to that on Lydia Townsend's *Moses* (cat. 21). Doggett would also have made the mat, this one strikingly painted in white, blue, and gold, and as such identical to one on Mary Crafts' *The Finding of Moses* at Winterthur, also from the Saunders/Beach Academy (Ring, *Mrs. Saunders' and Miss Beach's Academy*, p. 310 fig. 5).

The pencil inscription at the bottom of the silk appears to have been instructions for the text on the *églomisé* mat.

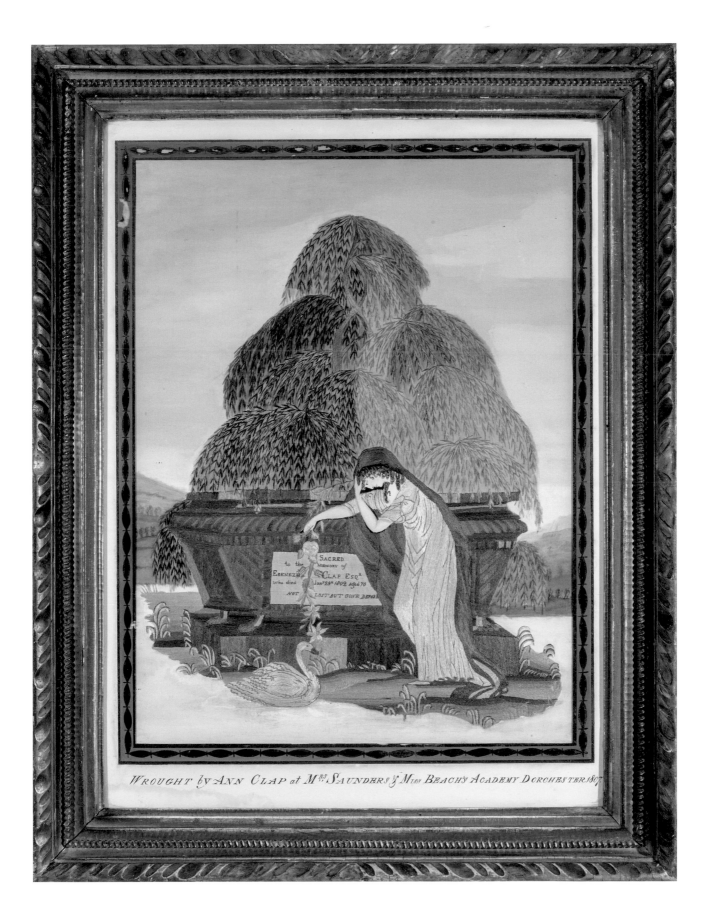

WROUGHT by ANN CLAP at M.RS SAUNDERS & MISS BEACH'S ACADEMY DORCHESTER 1807

Abigail Larkin, at Charlestown Academy, Charlestown, Massachusetts
Memorial to Mary and Ruth Larkin, about 1812–15
Silk embroidery thread and watercolor on silk, with appliqué
of printer's type on silk, and with original *églomisé* mat and
gilded frame, 20 x 18 1/8 in. (oval sight size)

Private collection

FIG. 12

Gideon Fairman (1774–1827)
"Memorial to Joseph Dennie," *The Port Folio* (new series) VII (1812), p. 67
Image courtesy of the American Antiquarian Society, Worcester, Massachusetts

23

HANNAH RUNEY

about 1795–1844

at

Charlestown Academy, Charlestown, Massachusetts

Memorial to Captain George Runey, about 1812

Silk embroidery thread and watercolor on silk, with appliqué of printer's type on silk, and with original *églomisé* mat and gilded frame, 19 3/8 x 17 1/2 in. (oval sight size); 24 x 21 1/8 in. (overall, including frame)

Signed and inscribed (at bottom of *églomisé* mat): Wrought by Hannah Runey; (with printing, on the silk appliqué): Sacred / TO THE MEMORY OF / CAPT. GEORGE RUNEY. / Obt. February 13, 1797, / AGED 37. / Now o'er his tomb the pensive friend shall mourn; / In silent sorrow tell the mournful tale; / Bid pity weave a garland for his urn, / And sigh his virtues to the passing gale.

During the later years of the eighteenth century and the early part of the nineteenth, embroideries memorializing a loved one became a staple of academies that provided instruction in various disciplines to young ladies.

This embroidery was done by Hannah Runey and was dedicated to the memory of her father, George Runey (1761–1797). The family lived in Charlestown, Massachusetts, a northern suburb of Boston. That George Runey was a ship captain is indicated not only in the printed inscription, but also by the presence of the anchor at the left of the monument.

The embroidery was executed at the Charlestown Academy, which was headed by Hannah Spofford. Certainly not coincidentally, another embroidery, executed by Abigail Larkin of Charlestown in memory of her sisters, Mary and Ruth (fig. 11), is almost identical in composition to the present work, curiously again including an anchor and varying largely in specific landscape elements and in the selection of the colors of the embroidery thread. Yet another embroidery, by Mary Frost of Charlestown, follows the same model, except now in a rectangular format (Ring, *American Needlework*, p. 67 no. 109 illus.).

It is likely that the schoolmistresses of the various girls' academies drew the patterns of the memorials or other subjects on the silk, some taken from prints, others possibly of their own invention. And after the girls completed their needlework, the schoolmistress or a local miniaturist then filled in the faces, hands, feet, etc.

Although needlework was taught to young ladies at an early age, the skill demonstrated in the Charlestown memorials suggests a greater maturity and skill. The Frost work could not date before 1812, the year in which the model for all three embroideries was published (fig. 12) and in which the last of the three

people being memorialized died. With respect to the Larkin piece, the two deceased sisters died in 1799, only one year after Abigail was born, suggesting that it, too, was likely done about 1812 or as late as 1815. And the Runey embroidery was likely executed about the same time since Hannah was probably only about two when her father died. Indeed, as legendary needlework specialist Betty Ring concludes, "although some mourning pieces were worked immediately following a death, the majority appear to be made as a record and a decoration, rather than an expression of current grief, and they were the result of fashion rather than melancholy" (*Girlhood Embroidery*, p. 21).

LIGHTING

24

JOHNSTON BROOKES & CO.

London (active 1814–35)

Retailed by

BEMIS & VOSE

Boston (active 1825–31)

Two-light Argand Chandelier, about 1825

Gilt and patinated bronze, with lamp mechanism, glass shades, blown, frosted, and wheel-cut, and glass chimneys, 31³/₈ in. high, 17⁷/₈ in. long, 10¹/₂ in. wide

Signed and inscribed, with embossed brass labels (attached to one burner tube): JOHNSTON BROOKES / & cº / MANUFACTURERS / LONDON.; (attached to the second burner tube): BEMIS & VOSE / BOSTON

Very few chandeliers signed by the London firm of Johnston Brookes & Co. have appeared, but those that have are of exceptional quality and have served as the basis of a number of credible attributions to them. The Johnston Brookes firm first appeared in the London City Directory for 1814 and remained in business until 1835.

Their exact connection to an American clientele has not previously been known, but Robert D. Mussey, Jr., and Clark Pearce, in conjunction with their research on the Boston cabinetmaking firms of Vose and Coates and Isaac Vose & Son, discovered documentation of a partnership between Isaac Vose, Jr. (1794–1872) and his cousin and brother-in-law Charles Bemis (1789–1874), who were in business as Bemis & Vose at 79 Market Street, Boston, from 1825, the year the cabinetmaking firm of Isaac Vose & Son ceased to operate, and 1831. Little is known of their activity, but they placed an advertisement in the Boston *Columbian Centinel* on August 10, 1825, announcing that they had "just received from London fifteen cases of Lamps, consisting of Center, Mantle, Side Lamps & c." (as cited by Mussey and Pearce, *Rather Elegant*, p. 194).

In addition to this two-light Argand chandelier, which is handsomely ornamented with a variety of classical devices, an imposing pair of cut-glass Argand lamps at the Corning Museum of Glass, Corning, New York (ibid., p. 195 fig. 211) is the only other known example that bears the labels of Bemis & Vose and Johnston Brookes, which, for the first time, signals that the very successful London firm was exporting their wares to the United States. Mussey and Pearce also cite documents recording a sale of a "chandelier &c. in Senate Chamber" for the Bulfinch State House in Boston for the then formidable sum of nearly $900, as well as several sales to private individuals.

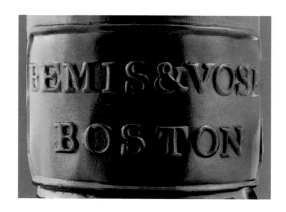

25

ENGLISH

probably Birmingham

Retailed by

LEWIS VERON & CO.

Philadelphia (active 1826–41)

Sinumbra Lamp, after 1826

Gilt and patinated bronze, with lamp mechanism,
glass shade, blown, frosted, and wheel-cut, and glass chimney,
30¼ in. high (to the top of chimney)

Inscribed (on embossed brass label, attached to the burner tube);
LEWIS VERON / & CO / PHILADELPHIA

Lewis Veron was probably the most important merchant in Philadelphia dealing in high-quality household furnishings during the early years of the nineteenth century. In 1815 his sister married Baldwin Gardiner, and two years later the two men joined forces as Gardiner & Veron & Company. The partnership was dissolved in 1826 in anticipation of Gardiner's relocating to New York (cats. 26, 34A, and 34B), and Veron continued on his own as Lewis Veron & Co. until 1841.

This sinumbra lamp, which bears the mark of Veron's eponymous firm, thus dates after 1826. It was certainly made in the English city of Birmingham, which was the center of the metalworking trade in England during the first half of the nineteenth century, and possibly by the firm of Thomas Messenger & Son.

The base of the lamp, which is largely finished with a dark brown patina, is ornamented with a series of gilt torchères around the base that were inspired by antique models. It is unknown whether imported lamps such as this arrived complete with their glass shades, or if the shades were supplied by an American firm.

26

ENGLISH

probably Birmingham

Retailed by

BALDWIN GARDINER

1796–1869

New York (active in New York, 1827–47)

Pair Argand Lamps, after 1827

Gilt and patinated bronze, with lamp mechanism, glass shades, blown and frosted, glass prisms, and glass chimneys; each, 17 in. high

Inscribed (on an embossed brass label, attached to the burner tube of each): B. GARDINER / N. YORK

Baldwin Gardiner was the leading retailer of luxurious household furnishings in New York. After leaving a partnership with his brother-in-law Lewis Veron (cat. 25) in Philadelphia in 1826, he opened his own "furnishing warehouse" at 149 Broadway, New York, in 1827, where he remained in business until 1836, before relocating in the Fall of that year to 39 Nassau Street, where he was an important factor in trade until 1847.

Although Gardiner dealt in a wide range of material, we know that lighting of various sorts was an important part of his business, as is evidenced by the considerable number of Argand lamps that have come down to us bearing his name on embossed brass labels attached to the burner tubes. Deborah Dependahl Waters, in her admirable catalogue of the silver collection at the Museum of the City of New York, quotes one of his advertisements, in which he offers "a very extensive assortment of new style MANTEL, CENTRE, & ASTRAL LAMPS, surpassing in CHOICE PATTERNS all former importations" (p. 343), which confirms the period appetite for "new" and fashionable.

This pair of lamps is particularly distinguished for its small scale and the vigorous paw feet, dolphins, and eagles that enrich the composition.

27

ENGLISH

probably Birmingham

Monumental Double Argand Lamp with Serpent Arms,
about 1820

Bronze and brass, with dark brown patina, with lamp mechanism,
glass shades, blown, frosted, and wheel-cut, and glass chimneys,
22³⁄₄ in. high, 21¹⁄₂ in. wide, 10¹⁄₂ in. deep (overall)

This double Argand lamp is distinguished by its massive scale,
mute testimony to the proportions of some of the town houses
and country seats that proliferated in the United States during
the 1820s. Certainly a product of one of the numerous manufactories in the metalworking center of Birmingham, England,
the lamp is nearly identical to a three-arm example in the collection of The Metropolitan Museum of Art, which bears the
embossed brass label of retailers J. & I. Cox of New York, themselves British imports from Birmingham.

The lamp features a pair of very bold bent knees resting on
robust paw feet, all mounted on a triangular platform with incurvate sides, Greek keys, a flattened urn that served as a fuel
tank, various classical borders, and serpents wrapped around
each of the arms, all based upon models from classical antiquity.

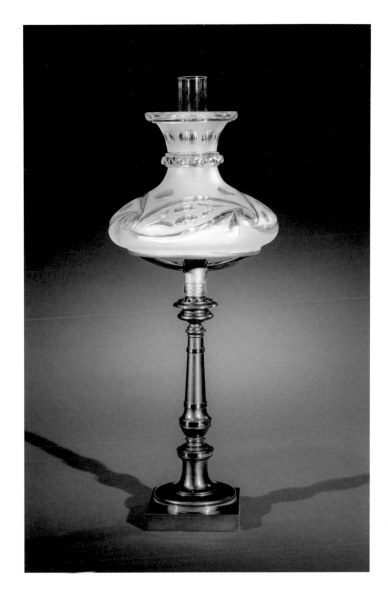

WILLIAM CARLETON

Boston (active about 1820–60)

Small Sinumbra Lamp, about 1830

Gilt and patinated bronze, with lamp mechanism, glass shade, blown, frosted, and wheel-cut, and glass chimney, 18½ in. high (to the top of chimney)

Signed and inscribed (on embossed brass label atatched to the burner tube): MANUFACTURED BY / W. CARLETON / BOSTON

During the early years of the nineteenth century, there were many inventions in the field of lighting that resulted in the more efficient illumination of interiors. In the wake of the development of the Argand lamp by the Swiss chemist Ami Argand (1759–1803) in 1783, the American Benjamin Thompson (1753–1814), also known as Count Rumford, invented a lamp mechanism that was intended to reduce the shadow cast by Argand's large urn-shaped fuel tank by using a circular tank for fuel, which, as he wrote, "got rid of all shadows preceding from the lamp." Popularly referred to as an astral, or sinumbra (without shadow), lamp, it was patented as a "Lamp Astrale" by the Frenchman Bordier-Marcet in 1809 and 1810, and for a couple of decades was an extremely popular method of lighting.

Although much of the lighting used in the United States during the Neo-Classical period was imported from England

and France, certain businesses here did produce a variety of lighting devices. This diminutive sinumbra lamp bears the same type of embossed metal label found on numerous lamps made in England, oftentimes with the names of American retailers (cats. 24, 25, and 26), but the text "MANUFACTURED BY / W. CARLETON / BOSTON" is clearly meant to distinguish it from similar imports. Ultimately, Carleton became one of the country's largest manufacturers of oil lamps and gas fixtures. His professional prowess earned him a place on the boards of the New England Glass Company, at Cambridge, Massachusetts, and the Boston & Sandwich Glass Company, at Sandwich, Massachusetts, one or both of which presumably supplied him with the beautiful frosted and cut-glass shades that typically accompanied his lamps.

29A

HENRY N. HOOPER

Boston (active about 1832–68)

Sinumbra Lamp, 1832–35

Patinated and gilt bronze, with lamp mechanism, glass shade, blown, frosted, and wheel-cut, and glass chimney, 25¾ in. high (to top of chimney)

Signed and inscribed (on embossed brass label attached to the burner tube): MANUFACTURED BY / H. N. HOOPER & Cº. / BOSTON; (cast into the upper side of the iron weight in the base): H. N. HOOPER & CO. BOSTON

Although it is likely that most—probably all—of the lighting sold by such retailers of household furnishings as Baldwin Gardiner in New York (cat. 26) and Lewis Veron in Philadelphia (cat. 25) was imported, Henry Hooper in Boston was actually the manufacturer of the lighting that he offered for sale. After working as a maker of mathematical instruments, he established his own firm in 1832 and developed an extensive line that included chandeliers, girandoles, candelabra, and lamps of many kinds, first in a Neo-Classical taste, as in this example (cat. 29A), and later in more florid designs that parallel the Rococo Revival furniture of Joseph Meeks & Son (active 1836–59) and John Henry Belter (active 1844–63).

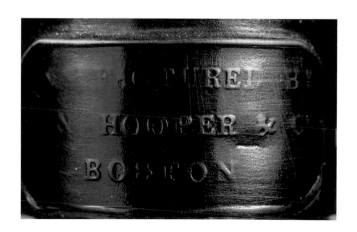

Lamps of this kind combined a circular, shadowless fuel tank with an Argand burner that, through improved combustion, provided a brighter light than had previously been possible.

The frosted and cut shade of exceptional quality was probably made at one of the local glass houses, possibly the New England Glass Company at Cambridge, or the Boston & Sandwich Glass Company at Sandwich.

Hooper also produced a limited number of student lamps (cat. 29B) of a form that Thomas Webster, in his *Encyclopedia*

29B

HENRY N. HOOPER

Boston (active about 1832–68)

Student Lamp, 1832–35

Gilt bronze, in a matte and burnished finish, with painted and
gilt-brass shade, lamp mechanism, and glass chimney, 20 in. high

Signed and inscribed (on embossed brass label attached to the
burner tube): MANUFACTURED BY / H. N. HOOPER & Cº. /
BOSTON

of Domestic Economy (1845), called a "university lamp," which
was likely intended as a desk lamp, as seen in Charles Willson
Peale's so-called "Lamplight Portrait" of his brother James of
1822 (The Detroit Institute of Arts, Michigan; Elam p. 17 fig. 7).

Like Carleton (cat. 28), Hooper proudly proclaimed that he
had "manufactured" his lamps in Boston. Indeed, in his book,
*Metalwork in Early America: Copper and its Alloys from the
Winterthur Collection*, Donald Fennimore, former Curator of
Metalwork at Winterthur, wrote that Hooper "exemplifies...
American entrepreneurs" who attempted to "supplant English
manufacturers" (p. 261).

Although a number of very simple Argand lamps marked
by Hooper have come down to us, relatively few student lamps
are known.

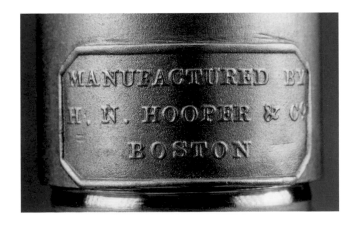

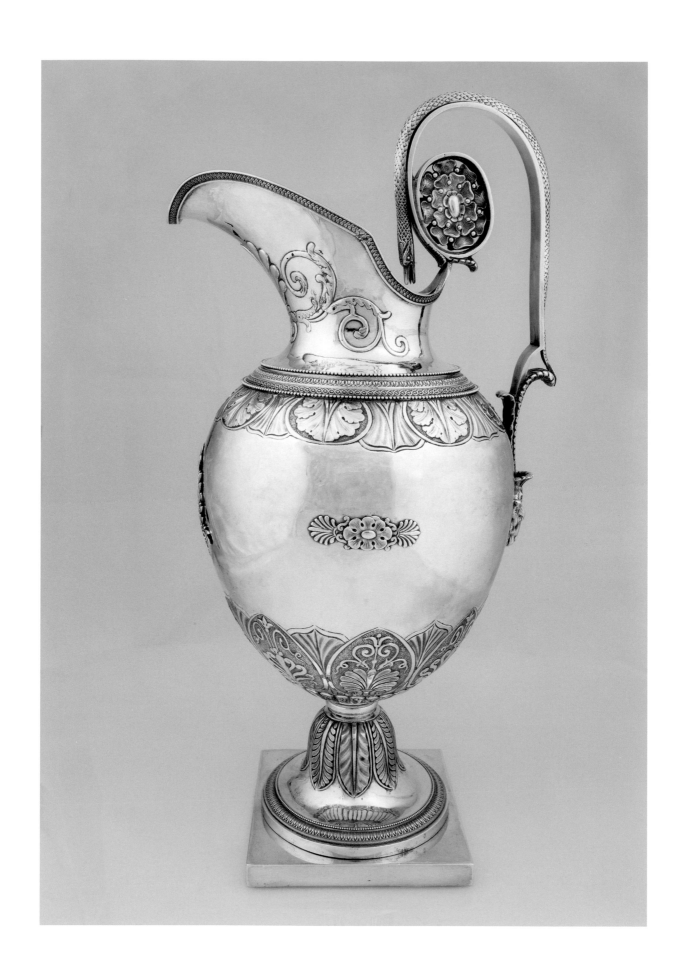

SILVER

30

SIMON CHAUDRON
1758–1846

Philadelphia

Covered Ewer, about 1807–09

Silver, 16½ in. high

Signed and inscribed (with touch, in ribbon, under base): CHAUDRON; (with engraving, within wreath, under spout): AMC; (below wreath): A Gift of Gratitude

Weight: 60.3 oz. Troy

Jean Simon Chaudron was born in Vignery, in the Champagne district of France. After studying watchmaking and silversmithing in Switzerland, he emigrated to the French colony of Saint-Domingue (now Haiti) in the Caribbean in 1784, and then, following an uprising there, in 1793 he moved to Philadelphia where he opened a shop that dealt in jewelry, watches, and imported silver. Gradually, he added silver of his own manufacture to his inventory.

In the style of the French Empire, this covered ewer probably dates to before 1809, in which year Chaudron took his apprentice, Anthony Rasch, as his partner (see cat. 31). The design reflects that of such Parisian silversmiths as Martin-Guillaume-Biennais (1764–1843) and Jean-Baptiste-Claude Odiot (1763–1850) and others displaying the style and motifs of the early Napoleonic period. Since Chaudron had left Europe by 1784, his source of influence is unclear, but he may have returned to France on an undocumented trip or trips, or possibly he saw pieces of French silver that had been imported, perhaps even by himself for sale in his own shop. Or, perhaps more simply, he could have referred to Thomas Hope's recently published *Household Furniture and Interior Decoration* (1807), where plate 49 shows a ewer with a related handle and mask below the handle, and plate 52 pictures another ewer with a serpent handle and similar leaves around the base of the body.

This covered ewer is extremely close in design to one (fig. 13) that was included in Wendy Cooper's comprehensive exhibition, *Classical Taste in America, 1800–1840*, where it was dated to 1807–11 (p. 156 fig. 114), curiously overlapping with the working dates of Chaudron's and Rasch. That piece also bears a touch reading "STER•AMERI•MAN•," a mark that appears on most of the silver produced by the Chaudron and Rasch partnership, indicating that Chaudron had already adopted this phrase before his formal association with Rasch.

Although at first glance the two ewers appear to be identical, except for the inclusion of the square base on the present piece, their program of ornament actually differs considerably, from the die-rolled borders around the neck to the *repoussé* patterns at the neck and at the tops and bottoms of the body. Even the manner in which the serpent is applied to the handle and the handle is attached to the body varies, as do the form of the leafy finials on the covers, and the position of the rosettes on the handles.

Clearly, Chaudron was of the same mind as his French-born contemporary, Charles-Honoré Lannuier, who in making his various card tables with caryatid supports never repeated himself except in original pairs.

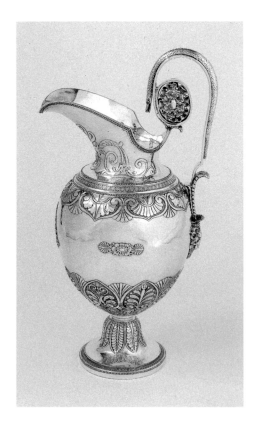

FIG. 13

Simon Chaudron
Covered Ewer,
about 1807–09
Silver, 16¼ in. high
Private collection

31

CHAUDRON'S & RASCH

SIMON CHAUDRON

1758–1846

&

ANTHONY RASCH

about 1778–about 1859

Philadelphia (active together, 1809–12)

Ewer, about 1809–12

Silver, 13 in. high

Signed and inscribed (with touches, in ribbons, on the bottom): CHAUDRON'S & RASCH / STER•AMERI•MAN•

Weight: 39.9 oz. Troy

The partnership of Simon Chaudron and Anthony Rasch brought together two of the most talented American silversmiths of the Neo-Classical period. In 1793 Chaudron settled in Philadelphia, where he opened a shop that dealt in jewelry, watches, and imported silver. Soon he began to make his own silver, and eventually he took Anthony Rasch as an apprentice.

Rasch was born in Germany, where he was trained as a silversmith. Clearly, Chaudron and Rasch established a good working relationship, and by 1809 they formed the partnership of Chaudron's & Rasch, which lasted until 1812. After that, they worked independently.

Chaudron first continued in business in Philadelphia, but after 1820 he settled in Demopolis, Alabama, where he remained until 1825, when he moved to Mobile. Rasch also initially remained in Philadelphia, but he, too, became a Southerner, settling in New Orleans where he was active from 1820 until his death about 1859.

Extremely few pieces by the short-lived Chaudron's & Rasch partnership are known, but the quality of their work establishes the partnership as one without peer in Federal Philadelphia.

This ewer is perfectly proportioned, and the decoration of eight large *repoussé* acanthus leaves around the body and four bands of delicate die-rolled ornament work together to create a flawless composition.

In 1817, several years after the end of the partnership, Chaudron asserted to the Baltimore silver trade, where assaying, or confirming the exact weight and content of silver, was a standard practice, that "there is no assay law in this City [i.e., Philadelphia], that our Word & stamp are sufficient to all our Customers with regard to the quality of the Silver manufactured by us; that we never manufacture any Silver of a lower quality than Spanish Dollars" (as quoted by Waters, p. 339).

This ewer bears the standard Chaudron's & Rasch mark in a ribbon, as well as their usual "STER•AMERI•MAN•," also in a ribbon, which may be an abbreviation for Sterling of American Manufacture.

32A

FLETCHER & GARDINER

THOMAS FLETCHER

1787–1866

&

SIDNEY GARDINER

1785–1827

Philadelphia (active together, 1811–27)

Five-piece Tea/Coffee Service, about 1815

Silver, with wooden handles, ebonized

Coffee pot: 9½ in. high

Signed and inscribed (with touches, on the bottom of each piece): F&G / PHILADA.; (with engraving, on one side of each piece): ELJ; (on the other side of each): SCJ

Weight: 165 oz. Troy gross

Without question, the body of silver produced by the firm of Thomas Fletcher and Sidney Gardiner, and Thomas Fletcher alone subsequent to Gardiner's early death in 1827, was the finest made in Federal America. Although they have been celebrated for an amazing array of presentation pieces, they also made a considerable variety of the best household silver.

Likely made not long after the firm of Fletcher & Gardiner moved from Boston to Philadelphia in 1811, this tea and coffee service (cat. 32A) displays many of the most popular devices of the Neo-Classical period, including paw feet, eagle spouts on the two pots, an eagle topping the handle of the creamer, female masks on the sugar bowl and waste bowl, and two patterns of die-rolled borders. The set is nearly identical to one included in

3 2 B

F L E T C H E R & G A R D I N E R

T H O M A S F L E T C H E R

1 7 8 7 – 1 8 6 6

&

S I D N E Y G A R D I N E R

1 7 8 5 – 1 8 2 7

Philadelphia (active together, 1811–27)

Chalice

Silver, 7⅞ in. high

Signed and inscribed (with round seal touch, on the bottom):
FLETCHER & GARDINER / PHILA; (with engraving,
on one side of vessel): MJF

Weight: 16 oz. 10 dwts. Troy

the exhibition, *Silversmiths to the Nation: Thomas Fletcher &
Sidney Gardiner: 1808–1842*, organized by Donald Fennimore
and Ann Wagner at Winterthur and circulated among three museums in 2007–08 (Fennimore and Wagner, p. 116 no. 5 illus.).
At the substantial weight of 165 oz. Troy gross, it demonstrates
the outstanding quality of the best of American silver of the
Neo-Classical period.

Another piece from the Fletcher & Gardiner partnership is a
chalice (cat. 32B). Although a piece identical in form was included
in the 2007–08 Fletcher & Gardiner exhibition as a "Goblet"
(ibid., pp. 156–57 no. 30 illus.), suggesting that it was intended
as a drinking vessel, it actually bears a dedicatory inscription, indicating that it was intended primarily as a presentation piece,
albeit one of more modest scale than the firm's more monumental
examples. Similarly, the present piece was made for the yet
unidentified "MJF," whose initials are engraved on one side, and
it is likely that it, too, was intended to mark a landmark event
in life, rather than serving purely as a utilitarian object.

From such massive presentation pieces as the pair of urns
presented by the Merchants of Pearl Street, New York, to Gov-
ernor DeWitt Clinton in 1824 (The Metropolitan Museum of
Art, New York; ibid., pp. 171–73 no. 43) to the humblest, un-
patterned teaspoon, the firms of Fletcher & Gardiner, and
Thomas Fletcher alone produced an amazing array of silver between 1808 and 1842. Its rarity today may be a function of its
considerable weight, attesting to its superb quality, which could
have been a motivation to melt down a number of pieces at a time
when nineteenth-century American silver was not in favor.

33

T H O M A S   F L E T C H E R

1 7 8 7 – 1 8 6 6

Philadelphia (active alone, 1 8 2 7 – 4 2)

Monumental Ewer, about 1 8 3 5

Silver, 1 5 7/16 in. high

Signed and inscribed (with oval seal touch, on the bottom):
T. FLETCHER / PHILAD.

Weight: 48 oz. Troy

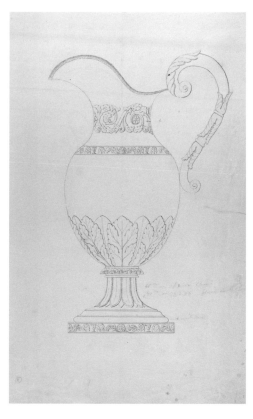

FIG. 14
Attributed to Thomas Fletcher
Design for a Water Pitcher, about 1 8 3 5
Pen and brown ink on cream wove paper, 1 9 7/8 x 1 2 in.

The Metropolitan Museum of Art, The Elisha Whittelsey Collection,
The Elisha Whittelsey Fund, 1 9 5 3 (5 3.6 5 2.2 0)
Image © The Metropolitan Museum of Art

In 1 9 5 3, the Print Department at The Metropolitan Museum of Art acquired an important trove of ornament drawings by the firms of Fletcher & Gardiner, and Thomas Fletcher, which provided an early clue to the range and quality of their work long before many of the related objects had come to light.

The recent discovery of this monumental ewer by Thomas Fletcher clearly relates to a drawing (fig. 14) in this group, one published by Beth Carver Wees in Chapter Six of the catalogue of the 2 0 0 7 – 0 8 Fletcher & Gardiner exhibition (Fennimore and Wagner, p. 99). Wees records various inscriptions on the drawing, including "45 oz ea at $2.50 chased" and "40 oz ea at $2.25 plain neck and foot," indicating that this model, like others, could be had in various configurations, and at different prices. Wees explains the notes and pricing on the drawing:

> a chased version of the pitcher, weighing 45 troy ounces, would cost $2.50 per ounce, or $112.50. With a plain neck and foot, the weight dropped to 40 ounces and the cost to $2.00 per ounce, or $80.00. Small "x" marks, indicating possible omissions, are placed beside the neck ornament, the chasing on the foot, and one of the steps on the foot above the plinth. These cryptic notes illuminate the process of manufacture: thicker silver was needed to accommodate the chasing; the neck and foot decoration was to be chased rather than cast and applied; and the narrow ornamental bands at the waist and on the plinth were presumably die-rolled (p. 99).

Based upon the inscription on the drawing and an examination of the ewer itself, the piece emerges as an example of the more expensive of the two options that are specified. The change of the design of the die-rolled border around the base and the *repoussé* band around the lower part of the bulbous section would not have been a factor in increasing or decreasing the cost of the piece, as the *repoussé*, or "chased," border of anthemia and acanthus leaves would have demanded the same thicker silver outlined in the pricing. Wees reads the design drawing as indicating a chased band around the neck, but, now, from the actual piece of silver with its elaborate collar of cast ornament of flowers, berries, and acanthus leaves, it would appear that the Fletcher shop might always have anticipated using an applied band.

The drawing can be dated to about 1 8 3 5, which would thus likely be the date of the ewer as well.

34 A

BALDWIN GARDINER

1 7 9 1 – 1 8 6 9

New York (active in New York, 1827–47)

Round Cake Basket with Reticulated Border and Handle

Silver, 11 in. high (with handle raised), 12¼ in. diameter

Signed and inscribed (with touches, on the bottom): B • GARDINER [in serrated rectangle] / [pseudo-hallmark of head in profile to right] / [pseudo-hallmark of lion] / S; (on center of handle): Gibbons

Weight: 48 oz. Troy

Baldwin Gardiner was the younger brother of Sidney Gardiner of the firm of Fletcher & Gardiner. His earliest employment was in their Boston establishment, where they were active from 1808 to 1811. Not long after moving with them to Philadelphia in 1811, he married Louise-Leroy Veron, sister of the wives of both Fletcher and Gardiner in 1815, in which year he opened his own store dealing in "fancy hardware." In 1817, he partnered with Lewis Veron (cat. 25), his wife's brother, in Gardiner, Veron & Company, retailers of household goods, an association that lasted until 1826. In the following year he moved to New York, and opened a "furnishing warehouse," which became the most important retailer of luxury household goods in New York.

By the early 1830s, Gardiner established his own silver manufactory, and there he produced a stunning array of pieces ranked at the top of New York production of the time. Among his finest

FIG. 15

Harvey Lewis (1783–1835), New York
Round Footed Basket with Handle
Silver, 10¾ in. diameter
Collection of Hirschl & Adler Galleries, New York

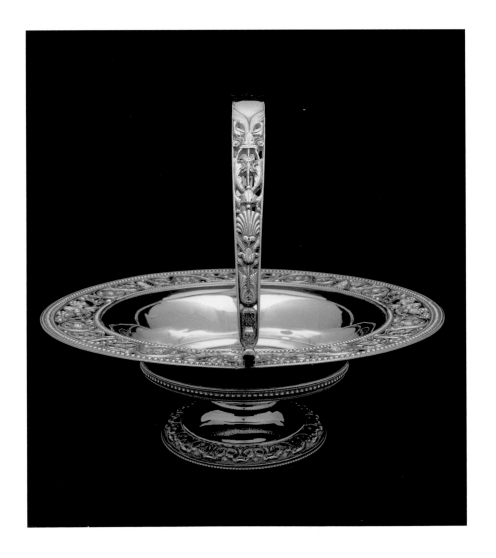

pieces is a newly discovered *Round Cake Basket* (cat. 34A), which, as a period inscription reveals, was made for a member of the Gibbons family. The basket is ornamented with a series of die-rolled borders in a fashion typical of the period, but is particularly distinguished by the cast openwork border consisting of flowers, acanthus leaves, and anthemia, somewhat reminiscent of the design of a basket by Philadelphian Harvey Lewis (fig. 15; and Cooper, p. 180 no. 138 illus.). The handle, too, with its own acanthus leaves, shells, and other Neo-Classical devices, adds to the impact of the piece as a masterpiece of its time.

Another unusual piece of silver by Baldwin Gardiner is a *Cruet Frame* (cat. 34B), which is supported by a quartet of feet formed by winged couchant lions, and is otherwise ornamented with cast acanthus leaves on the handle, and a bold die-rolled border around the base.

3 4 B

B A L D W I N   G A R D I N E R

1 7 9 1 – 1 8 6 9

New York (active in New York, 1827–47)

Cruet Frame

Silver, with clear glass bottles, blown and cut, $11\frac{1}{4}$ in. high, $11\frac{5}{8}$ in. diameter (at the feet)

Signed (with touches, on the edge of base): B • GARDINER [in serrated rectangle] / [pseudo-hallmark of lion, twice] / [pseudo-hallmark of head in profile to right, twice] / G [twice]

Weight: 50 oz. 10 dwt. Troy

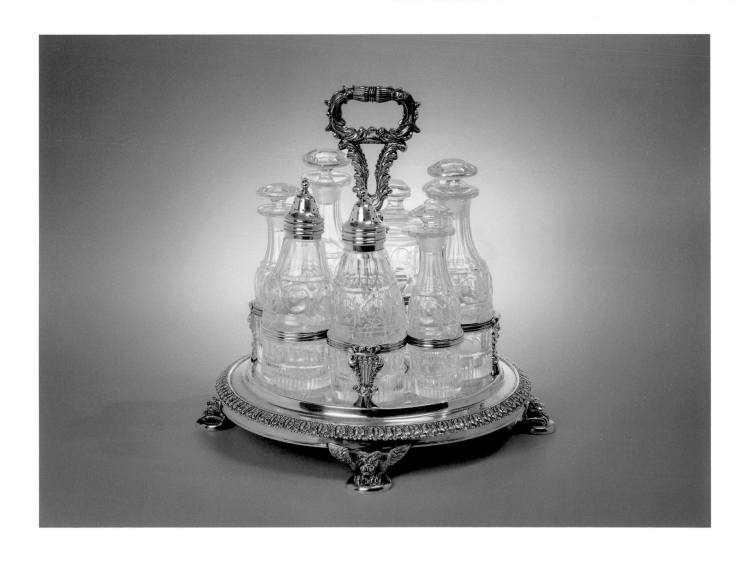

CERAMICS

35

TUCKER FACTORIES

Philadelphia (active 1826–38)

Pair Flared Vases with Floral Decoration, about 1832–38

Porcelain, partially painted and gilded, 8½ in. high,
8¹⁄₁₆ in. diameter (at the top)

In an attempt to bring the manufacture of hard-paste porcelain to the United States, in 1826 William Ellis Tucker organized a business to make porcelain in Philadelphia. In its various incarnations, Tucker operated a porcelain business until 1838, which makes it the first commercially successful manufactory of porcelain in America.

With a business that made a variety of porcelain, varying from small, generic, and practical pieces, with little or no ornamentation, to larger and more fully finished decorative objects, the Tucker factories emulated the production of French porcelain manufactories, and although rarely is it difficult to distinguish a piece of Tucker porcelain from its French prototypes, the goal was, nevertheless, to be as close as possible to what we today call "Old Paris" porcelain.

One of the most popular forms produced in France, both in porcelain and glass, was the flared beaker-shaped vase, which was made in a number of sizes and with a full range of decoration. The Tucker shape and pattern book, covering the years 1832–38 (collection of the Department of Prints, Drawings, and Photography at the Philadelphia Museum of Art), illustrates the wide variety of decoration that was available on pieces of this form. None are more elaborate than that of the present pair, which includes a band of clusters of flowers centered by a pink rose set against a white background dotted with gold "snowflakes," the whole above a wide border with vertical, gilded stripes, and all placed within geometric and floral borders. This pattern was one of Tucker's most popular, and appears otherwise on a remarkable pair of monumental vases with gilt-bronze handles (Philadelphia Museum of Art; Frelinghuysen, p. 101 illus.), and an extensive tea and coffee service and a matching pair of reticulated compotes (Armstrong, p. 194 illus. at upper right). As the premier examples of their form, these vases take their place among the finest works produced by the Tucker Factories.

36A

TUCKER FACTORIES

Philadelphia (active 1826–38)

Urn with Caryatid Handles, with a Floral Bouquet and a Landscape en Grisaille

Porcelain, partially painted in polychrome and *grisaille*, and gilded, with an iron tie-rod for assembly, 11¾ in. high

Many of the pieces produced by the Tucker Factories were utilitarian, but they also made a number of pieces that were purely decorative. Among these is a vase painted with a floral bouquet on one side and an imaginative landscape in sepia on the other (cat. 36A), which are framed by a pair of handles of winged female figures that are directly cribbed from "Old Paris" prototypes.

A second vase (cat. 36B) is of the same general form, although of more delicate scale, and is decorated on one side with an arrangement of flowers, and, on the back, the initials in gold "ACW" for Andrew Craig Walker, who was an important modeler at the Tucker Factories. The vase is also dated 1828, just two years into the Tucker enterprise, suggesting that even their early work was quite sophisticated in its emulation of fine French porcelain.

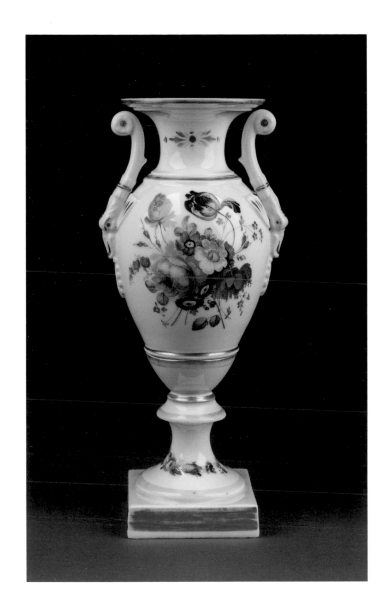
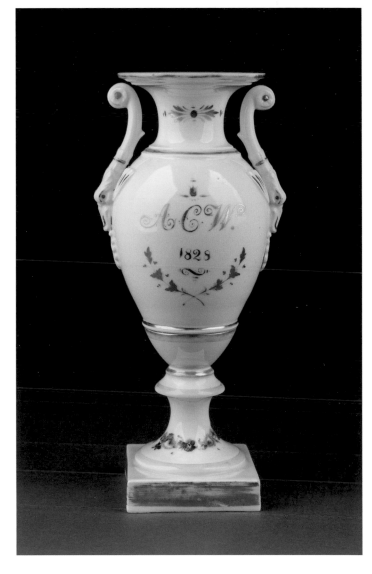

36B

TUCKER FACTORIES

Philadelphia (active 1826–38)

The Andrew Craig Walker Handled Urn, 1828

Porcelain, partially painted in polychrome and gilded, with an
iron tie-rod for assembly, 10^{11}/$_{16}$ in. high

Inscribed and dated (on the back): ACW. / 1828

37

CHINESE

for the American Market

Chinese Export Porcelain Covered Two-section
Vegetable Dish from the Joseph R. Sims
"Washington Memorial" Service, about 1800–05

Porcelain, partially painted and gilded, 6¾ in high, 11 in. long,
9¼ in. deep

Inscribed (with monogram, in overglaze red and gold, twice,
in oval reserves in border of cover): JRS

During the later years of the eighteenth century and the first part of the nineteenth century, a number of very large porcelain dinner services, some consisting of as many as several hundred pieces, were custom made in China for American families. The decoration consisted of anything from a simple monogram to elaborate polychrome depictions of the Order of the Cincinnati, the Arms of the State of New York, clipper ships, eagles, and so forth.

Of all the decorations intended specifically for the American market, none is more fascinating than that on a service decorated with Washington's tomb inscribed "WASHINGTON," surmounted by an eagle and set against a weeping willow. A few pieces from this service have been published as bearing the painted and gilded monogram "JRL," which has been variously identified as standing for Judith and Robert Lewis, the son and daughter-in-law of George Washington's sister, Betty, and her husband, Fielding Lewis, and, alternatively, John R. Latimer, a Philadelphia merchant engaged in the China trade from about 1815 to 1833. Actually, the monogram is correctly read not as "JRL" but as "JRS." Indeed, a letter dated January 12, 1824, from Louisa E. Ewing to her brother Maskell C. Ewing, which accompanied the donation of three pieces from this service to Kenmore, an eighteenth-century house museum in Fredericksburg, Virginia, establishes that this service originally belonged to Joseph R. Sims of Philadelphia. In describing the interior of Sims' residence and some of its contents, Ewing wrote:

> The week before christmass [*sic*] I spent in town and as Sims's furniture oposite [*sic*] to Uncle Pattersons [*sic*] was sold I went to see it. The front parlour had an elegant organ which took up one side of the room, there was another organ for chanting, and an old piano. The carpet was Turkish but very much worn, the chairs were mahogony [*sic*] with hair seats, very old fashioned and worn out…. The curtains were blue crimson and yellow damask with a portrait of washington in the center of the middle drapery, they were the handsomest I ever saw…. Upstairs was a very handsome library with glass ships, Chinese mandarines [*sic*], busts, paintings, marble figures etc. to fill it up. All the china had the tomb of Washington in the center of every piece. I have now given you a description of all that was worth notice (as quoted in "The Ewing Papers—Part Two," p. 43).

In keeping with Ewing's description of the various contents of the Sims' Philadelphia home as "worn," most of the pieces from this service are chipped, cracked, and abraded, suggesting that many pieces had been extensively used. By contrast, the present piece, one of the most elaborate pieces from this service, is in virtually uncirculated condition.

GLASS

38A

BAKEWELL, PAGE & BAKEWELL

Pittsburgh (active 1808–82)

Clear "Strawberry Diamond and Fan" Pitcher,
about 1820–25

Glass, blown and cut, 8¼ in. high

By virtue of the import of trained European glass blowers and engravers, some American cut glass from the early years of the nineteenth century was so close to Anglo-Irish and European prototypes that attribution can oftentimes be extremely difficult. However, the present pitcher, cut in the ubiquitous "Strawberry Diamond and Fan" design (cat. 38A), can confidently be ascribed to the Pittsburgh firm of Bakewell, Page & Bakewell because it is identical to a slightly smaller pair that descended in the Bakewell family, which, as Arlene Palmer writes, can serve as "the touchstone for specific Bakewell characteristics and assist… in clarifying attributions" (Palmer, p. 148 no. 51 illus.).

With respect to the monumental footed compote in the same pattern (cat. 38B), an attribution to Bakewell is less certain, although its scale and composition—its specific character—suggest an American origin, and probably, again, Bakewell.

By contrast, the remarkable pair of lamps with pressed bases and blown, cut, and engraved fonts, and pewter fittings (cat. 38C) is clearly American. When these lamps were first published by Ruth Webb Lee in her landmark *Sandwich Glass* in 1947 (p. 472 plate 191), they were attributed to the Boston & Sandwich Glass Company, which may still be correct, but now slightly complicated by Pittsburgh glass chronicler Lowell Innes's illustration of a lamp with an identical base and a simpler cut font, which he described as Pittsburgh, but with the disclaimer that "variations of this base were used in the East" (Innes, p. 238), possibly even referring to the present pair of lamps. Attribution aside, Lee's early description of them as "superlative" has not been mitigated in the ensuing seventy years, as the lamps remain the finest examples of their type that have appeared. It is thus not surprising that they were selected to join the august company of objects that were included in The Metropolitan Museum's ground-breaking exhibition, *19th-Century America*, in 1970 (see Tracy et al., no. 57), where they were attributed to Sandwich.

38B

Attributed to

BAKEWELL, PAGE & BAKEWELL

Pittsburgh (active 1808–82)

Monumental Clear "Strawberry Diamond and Fan"
Footed Compote, about 1820–25

Glass, blown and cut, 7⅝ in. high, 11⅞ in. diameter

38C

Attributed to

BOSTON & SANDWICH
GLASS COMPANY

Sandwich, Massachusetts (active 1825–88)

Pair Clear Blown and Cut Whale Oil Lamps, about 1830–35

Glass, blown and cut, and pressed, with pewter burners,
13 1/16 in. high (to the top of the pewter burners)

39

NEW ENGLAND GLASS COMPANY

Cambridge, Massachusetts (active 1818–88)

or

BOSTON & SANDWICH
GLASS COMPANY

Sandwich, Massachusetts (active 1825–88)

Pair Opaque Blue Slag Lamps with Lion Bases, about 1830

Glass, pressed and blown-molded, with pewter collars,
9⅝ in. high (to the top of the pewter collars)

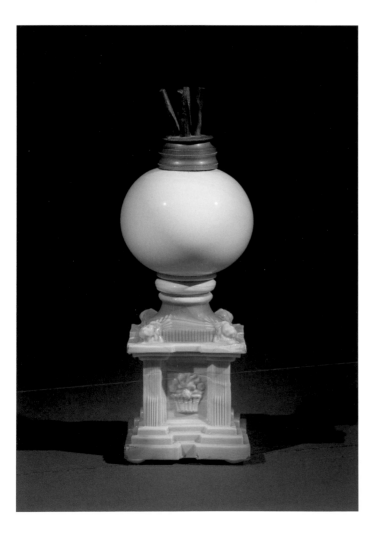

Although a very large quantity of blown and pressed whale oil lamps was produced by various New England glass manufactories in the second quarter of the nineteenth century, few would argue that this pair of blue slag lamps with monument bases and couchant lions at each corner is the rarest and the most dramatic of all. Lamps of this general type came in clear, opaque white, and deep opalescent, with bases in two sizes, and free-blown spherical, conical, and cylindrical fonts. These lamps, first published by George S. and Helen McKearin in their *American Glass* in 1941 (p. 380, pl. 193 no. 2), are unique both in their vertically paneled blown-molded fonts and in their unusual blue slag color, the latter of which is known only in two smaller lamps of more conventional form in the collections of Hirschl & Adler Galleries (fig. 16), and the Corning Museum of Glass, Corning, New York (Spillman, p. 202 no. 1790 illus.), as well as one with a blown-molded conical font at the Sandwich Glass Museum (Barlow and Kaiser, II, p. 77 no. 2077 illus.).

It is unclear where the numerous lion lamps of this general type were made. A few examples marked "N E G C O" (New England Glass Company) and "E.R.S.R." have appeared, leading to an attribution to Enoch Robinson and Spencer Richards, who were employees at the New England Glass Company, at Cambridge. On the other hand, the fact that an account book of the Boston & Sandwich Glass Company of the 1825–28 period (collection of The Edison Institute, Henry Ford Museum, Dearborn, Michigan) lists "lion head lamps" suggests a possible attribution to the Boston & Sandwich Glass Company as well.

FIG. 16

New England Glass Company, Cambridge, Massachusetts
or
Boston & Sandwich Glass Company, Sandwich, Massachusetts
Blue Slag Lamp with Lion Base, about 1830
Glass, pressed and blown, with pewter collar and burner, 9 in. high

Collection of Hirschl & Adler Galleries, New York

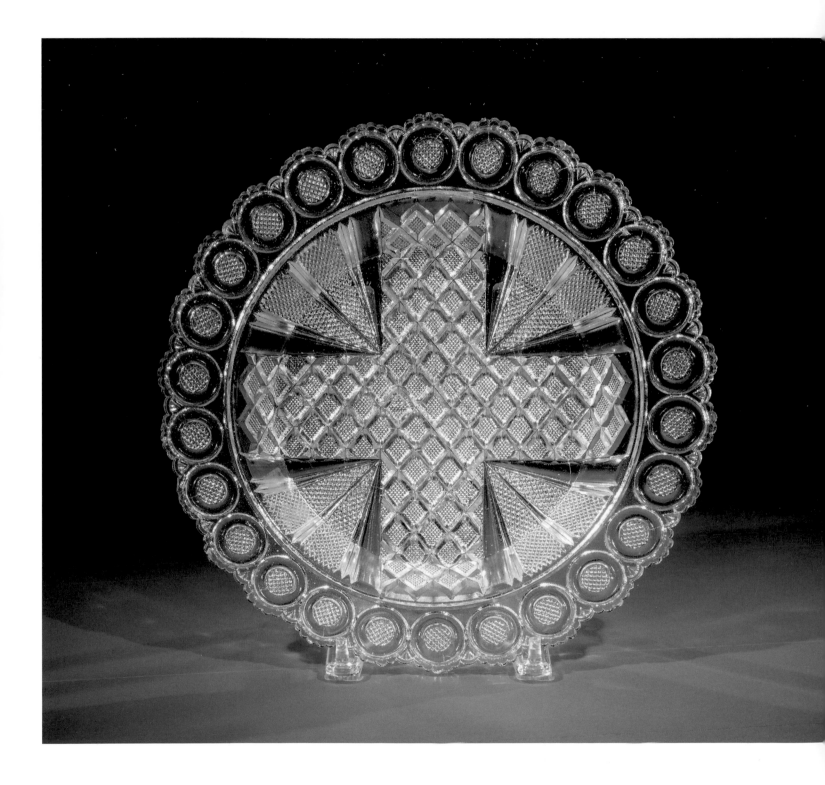

40A

Attributed to

BOSTON & SANDWICH
GLASS COMPANY

Sandwich, Massachusetts (active 1825–88)

or

NEW ENGLAND GLASS COMPANY

Cambridge, Massachusetts (active 1818–88)

Clear "Strawberry Diamond" Bowl with Cross, about 1830

Glass, pressed, 1¾ in. high, 12⅛ in. diameter

Although expensive cut glass of excellent quality (see cats. 38A and 38B) became a staple of wealthy and sophisticated households in the United States during the Neo-Classical period, some American glasshouses sought to replicate the look of this expensive imported and domestic glass with the new invention of pressed glass, which was developed at the Boston & Sandwich Glass Company, with offices in Boston and a manufactory in Sandwich, on Cape Cod. Glass pressing began in the later 1820s, but by the early 1830s various factories in New England were producing such works as this *"Strawberry Diamond" Bowl with Cross* (cat. 40A) that, in replicating the ubiquitous "Strawberry Diamond" pattern of fine cut glass, effectively reproduced the effect of the more expensive wares. The bowl may have been made at Sandwich, or possibly at the New England Glass Company, at Cambridge. Conceived and produced as a utilitarian object, subject to extensive use and consequent breakage, only a few are now known in the considerable size of this example.

From the same moment is a footed vase, which has always been known as the *"Cape Cod Lily" Footed Vase* (cat. 40B). Fragments excavated at the site of the Sandwich factory include a piece from a vase of this form, thus confirming its origin at Sandwich. Although, again, it is not unlikely that a number were made, only five beyond this example are known, which are now in the collections of The Metropolitan Museum of Art, New York; the Corning Museum of Glass, Corning, New York; the Detroit Institute of Arts, Michigan; the Chrysler Museum, Norfolk, Virginia; and the Sandwich Glass Museum, Sandwich.

40B

BOSTON & SANDWICH
GLASS COMPANY

Sandwich, Massachusetts (active 1825–88)

Clear "Cape Cod Lily" Footed Vase, about 1830

Glass, pressed, 7⅜ in. high

41A

BOSTON & SANDWICH
GLASS COMPANY

Sandwich, Massachusetts (active 1825–88)

*Deep Amethyst "Lacy" Compote in the
"Princess Feather" Pattern*, about 1835–45

Glass, pressed, 6¼ in. high, 10⅝ in. long, 8¾ wide

In the years following the production of such pieces as the *"Strawberry Diamond" Bowl with Cross* (cat. 40A) and the *"Cape Cod Lily" Footed Vase* (cat. 40B), there arose a desire to conceal impurities, and a new style of glass was developed with a stippled, or "lacy," background that would help to conceal various foreign particles. Most of these pieces were produced in clear, or colorless, glass, but occasionally colored pieces were made. Of these, the largest and most imposing was a compote in the "Princess Feather" pattern, which was made in sapphire blue, canary yellow, turquoise blue, wisteria, and the deep amethyst of this example (cat. 41A).

41B

BOSTON & SANDWICH
GLASS COMPANY

Sandwich, Massachusetts (active 1825–88)

Pair Deep Amethyst Elongated Loop Vases, about 1835–45

Glass, pressed and manipulated, 13⁷/₁₆ in. high

From roughly the same period is this pair *Deep Amethyst Loop Vases* (cat. 41B), also made at Sandwich, each of which started out as two pressed pieces, a base and a vase, which were joined, while hot, by a glass wafer, and the vases were then pulled out to their substantial height. They were first published and illustrated by the McKearins in their landmark book, *American Glass*, in 1941 (pl. 195 no. 1), and 77 years later the pair remains unique.

BIBLIOGRAPHY

Baldwin Gardiner
New York
Round Cake Basket with Reticulated Border and Handle
CAT. 34A

Armstrong, Tom. *An American Odyssey: The Warner Collection of American Fine and Decorative Arts*. New York: The Monacelli Press, 2001.

Barlow, Raymond E., and Joan E. Kaiser. *The Glass Industry in Sandwich*. Vol. 2. Downingtown, Pennsylvania: Schiffer Publishing Ltd. for Barlow-Kaiser Publishing Co., 1989.

Cooper, Wendy A. *Classical Taste in America, 1800–1840*. Exhib. cat., Baltimore: The Baltimore Museum of Art, 1993.

Elam, Charles H. *The Peale Family: Three Generations of American Artists*. Exhib. cat., Detroit: The Detroit Institute of Arts, 1967.

Elder, William Voss, III. *Baltimore Painted Furniture, 1800–1840*. Exhib. cat., Baltimore: The Baltimore Museum of Art, 1972.

"The Ewing Papers—Part Two." *The American Magazine and Historical Chronicle* 3 (Autumn–Winter 1987–88): 40–53.

Fales, DeCoursey. *The Fales Family of Bristol, Rhode Island: Ancestry of Haliburton Fales of New York*. Privately printed, 1919.

Feld, Elizabeth, and Stuart P. Feld. *Of the Newest Fashion: Masterpieces of American Neo-Classical Decorative Arts*. Exhib. cat., New York: Hirschl & Adler Galleries, 2001.

———. *The World of Duncan Phyfe: The Arts of New York, 1800–1847*. Exhib. cat., New York: Hirschl & Adler Galleries, 2011.

———. *Very Rich and Handsome: American Neo-Classical Decorative Arts*. Exhib. cat., New York: Hirschl & Adler Galleries, 2014.

Feld, Stuart P. *Neo-Classicism in America: Inspiration and Innovation, 1810–1840*. Exhib. cat., New York: Hirschl & Adler Galleries, 1991.

———. *Boston in the Age of Neo-Classicism, 1810–1840*. Exhib. cat., New York: Hirschl & Adler Galleries, 1999.

———. "Making an Uncollectible Collectible: American Silver, 1810–1840." *The Magazine Antiques* CLXXII (October 2007): 86–97.

Fennimore, Donald. *Metalwork in Early America: Copper and Its Alloys from the Winterthur Collection*. Winterthur, Delaware: The Henry Francis du Pont Winterthur Museum, 1996.

Fennimore, Donald L., and Robert T. Trump. "Joseph B. Barry, Philadelphia Cabinetmaker." *The Magazine Antiques* CXXXV (May 1989): 1212–25.

Fennimore, Donald L., and Ann Wagner. *Silversmiths to the Nation: Thomas Fletcher and Sidney Gardiner, 1808–1842*. Exhib. cat., Winterthur, Delaware: The Henry Francis du Pont Winterthur Museum, 2007.

Flanigan, J. Michael. *American Furniture from the Kaufman Collection*. Exhib. cat., Washington, D.C.: National Gallery of Art, 1986.

Foley, Paul J. *Willard's Patent Timepieces*. Norwell, Massachusetts: Roxbury Village Publishing, 2002.

Frelinghuysen, Alice Cooney. *American Porcelain, 1770–1920*. New York: The Metropolitan Museum of Art, 1989.

Gerdts, William H. *Thomas Birch (1779–1851): Paintings and Drawings*. Philadelphia: Philadelphia Maritime Museum, 1966.

Hawley, Henry. "Philadelphia Tables with Lyre Supports." *The Bulletin of The Cleveland Museum of Art* 75 (January 1988): 1–27.

Hope, Thomas. *Household Furniture and Interior Decoration*. London: Longman, Hurst, Rees, and Orme, 1807. Reprint, New York: Dover Publications, Inc., 1971.

Innes, Lowell. *Pittsburgh Glass, 1797–1891: A History and Guide for Collectors*. Boston: Houghton Mifflin Co., 1976.

Israel Sack, Inc. *American Antiques from Israel Sack Collection*. 10 vols. Washington, D.C.: Highland House Publishers, 1969–92.

Kenny, Peter M., Frances F. Bretter, and Ulrich Leben. *Honoré Lannuier, Cabinetmaker from Paris: The Life and Work of a French Ébéniste in Federal New York*. Exhib. cat., New York: The Metropolitan Museum of Art, 1998.

Kenny, Peter M., Michael K. Brown, Frances F. Bretter, and Matthew A. Thurlow. *Duncan Phyfe: Master Cabinetmaker in New York*. Exhib. cat., New York: The Metropolitan Museum of Art, 2011.

Kuronen, Darcy. "Early Pianomaking in Boston, 1790–1830." *Boston Furniture, 1700–1900*. Boston: Colonial Society of Massachusetts, 2016.

Lahikainen, Dean T. *Samuel McIntire: Carving an American Style*. Salem, Massachusetts: Peabody Essex Museum, 2007.

Lee, Ruth Webb. *Sandwich Glass: The History of the Boston and Sandwich Glass Company*. Northborough, Massachusetts: Privately printed, 1947.

McClelland, Nancy. *Duncan Phyfe and the English Regency, 1795–1830*. New York: William R. Scott, 1939.

McKearin, George S. and Helen. *American Glass*. New York: Crown Publishers, 1941.

The Metropolitan Museum of Art, New York. *A Walk through the American Wing*. New York: The Metropolitan Museum of Art, 2001.

Mussey, Robert D., Jr. *The Furniture Masterworks of John and Thomas Seymour*. Salem, Massachusetts: Peabody Essex Museum, 2003.

Mussey, Robert D., Jr., and Clark Pearce. "Classical Excellence in Boston: The Furniture of Isaac Vose, 1789–1825." *Boston Furniture, 1700–1900*. Boston: Colonial Society of Massachusetts, 2016.

———. *Rather Elegant Than Showy: The Classical Furniture of Isaac Vose*. Boston: The Massachusetts Historical Society, 2018.

Nylander, Richard C. "Framing the Interior: The Entrepreneurial Career of John Doggett." *Boston Furniture, 1700–1900*. Boston: Colonial Society of Massachusetts, 2016.

Palmer, Arlene. *Artistry and Innovation in Pittsburgh Glass, 1808–1882: From Bakewell & Ensell to Bakewell, Pairs & Company*. Pittsburgh: Frick Art & Historical Center, 2005.

Philadelphia Museum of Art. *Philadelphia: Three Centuries of American Art*. Exhib. cat., Philadelphia: Philadelphia Museum of Art, 1976.

Quimby, Ian M. G. *American Silver at Winterthur*. Winterthur, Delaware: The Henry Francis du Pont Winterthur Museum, 1991.

Ring, Betty. *Girlhood Embroidery: American Samplers & Pictorial Needlework, 1650–1850*. Vol. 1. New York: Alfred A. Knopf, 1963.

———. "Mrs. Saunders' and Miss Beach's Academy, Dorchester." The Magazine Antiques CX (August 1976): 302–12.

———. *American Needlework Treasures: Samplers and Silk Embroideries from the Collection of Betty Ring*. New York: E. P. Dutton in association with the Museum of American Folk Art, New York, 1987.

Robinson, Roger W., and Herschel B. Burt. *The Willard House and Clock Museum and The Willard Family Clockmakers*. Columbia, Pennsylvania: National Association of Watch and Clock Collectors, 1996.

Smith, George. *A Collection of Designs for Household Furniture and Interior Decoration in the Most Approved and Elegant Taste*. London: 1806–08. Reprint, New York: Praeger Publishers, 1970.

Smith, Robert C. "The Furniture of Anthony G. Quervelle, Part IV: Some Case Pieces." *The Magazine Antiques* CV (January 1974): 180–93.

Smith, Thomas Gordon. "Living with Antiques: Millford Plantation in South Carolina." *The Magazine Antiques* CLI (May 1997): 732–41.

Spillman, Jane Shadel. *American and European Pressed Glass in The Corning Museum of Glass*. Corning, New York: The Corning Museum of Glass, 1981.

Stoneman, Vernon C. *John and Thomas Seymour*. Boston: Special Publications, 1959.

Talbott, Page. "Boston Empire Furniture, Part I." *The Magazine Antiques* CVII (May 1975): 878–87.

———. "Seating Furniture in Boston, 1810–1835." *The Magazine Antiques* CXXXIX (May 1991): 956–69.

Tracy, Berry B., and William H. Gerdts. *Classical America, 1815–1845*. Exhib. cat., Newark, New Jersey: The Newark Museum, 1963.

Tracy, Berry B., Marilynn Johnson, Marvin D. Schwartz, and Suzanne Boorsch. *19th-Century America: Furniture and Other Decorative Arts*. Exhib. cat., New York: The Metropolitan Museum of Art, 1970.

Trump, Robert T. "Joseph B. Barry, Philadelphia Cabinetmaker." *The Magazine Antiques* CVII (January 1975): 159–63.

Waters, Deborah Dependahl. *Elegant Plate: Three Centuries of Precious Metals in New York City*. 2 vols. New York: Museum of the City of New York, 2000.

DESIGN

Elizabeth Finger

PRINTING

The Studley Press

PHOTOGRAPHY

All photographs by Eric W. Baumgartner, except:
Helga Photo Studio: pp. 13, 18, 20, 77

© The Metropolitan Museum of Art / Art Resource,
New York: pp. 11, 83

Image courtesy of the American Antiquarian Society,
Worcester, Massachusetts: p. 64 (fig. 12)

FRONT COVER

Card Table with Lyre Base (detail), about 1815
Philadelphia
Cat. 3

FRONTISPIECE

Recamier (detail), about 1825
Attributed to Joseph Barry, Philadelphia
Cat. 1

CONTENTS

Covered Ewer (detail), about 1807–09
Simon Chaudron, Philadelphia
Cat. 30

© 2018 Hirschl & Adler Galleries, Inc.

Library of Congress Control Number: 2018913199

ISBN: 978-1-937941-14-7